Listen, Bright Angel

Books by Edwin Corle

Mojave

Fig Tree John

People on the Earth

Burro Alley

Solitaire

Desert Country

Coarse Gold

Listen, Bright Angel

Listen, Bright Angel

By

EDWIN CORLE

Duell, Sloan and Pearce · New York

To

Horace W. Armstrong

. . . and if this expedition has any right to success or survival, then listen to a scientist's prayer, O Bright Angel of Immortality. . . .

Contents

CONTENTS

I

Central Character

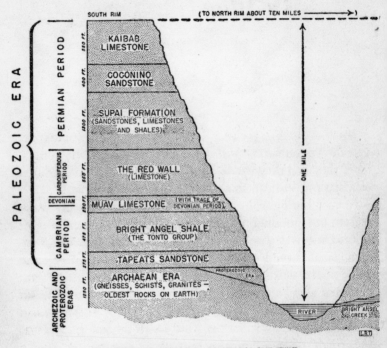

SCHEMATIC CROSS SECTION OF THE
GRAND CANYON FROM SOUTH RIM TO
RIVER AT GRAND CANYON VILLAGE
(LOOKING WEST). DEPTHS OF VARIOUS
STRATA ARE APPROXIMATE FIGURES.

An Island in Time

THE world was in a fine state; nobody was on earth. And it was a lucky thing they weren't, for if they had they would have been cooked to the condition of a sizzling steak in something less than one second.

In fact the figure is inept. On the centigrade scale water boils at one hundred degrees. The temperature of the surface of the earth was about six thousand degrees centigrade. A sizzling steak would have been ice-cold by comparison, and could not have existed for one second. Even such heat-resistant elements as platinum and carbon were not only melted, but they were in a state of gaseous nebulae. The world was a ball of hot gas, and hot is not the word for it. Its temperature was the result of sub-atomic energy from the interior which reached the amazing value of twenty million degrees. It is beyond comprehension. If the electric heater in your bathroom could be stepped up to this level it would instantly set fire to anything and everything within a radius of many thousand miles.

The reason for all this was that the earth had just been born. Because of the gravitational pull of a passing star it had been wrenched and torn from the body of its mother, the sun. It was made up entirely of sun-stuff. This was three billion years ago.

If there is one thing that the earth has always had in abundance, that thing is time. If time is money, the earth is a pluto-crat—at least, from the point of view of little man. But when the first crust formed and the ball of hot gas had passed through a state of liquefaction to solidity, living things had not yet appeared. All this was the preparatory stage—the first billion years were the hardest—and the earth, painfully and slowly, was getting ready to produce life.

The crust deepened until the outer surface had a depth of forty miles; and the internal heat, slowly diminishing, was sealed in the interior. This was the Archeozoic era, geologi-cally speaking, and while much of the surface was covered with water, the oldest known rocks were formed and re-formed and folded and tilted and fused. There was igneous in-trusion and volcanic action; the crust shrank and cracked and faulted; mountains were thrown up and worn down. There was plenty of time for all this for another eight hundred mil-lion years were going by. If there was any life all traces of it were eradicated in the geologic fusion, and it is probable that there was none. These Archean rocks are not to be found readily on the face of the earth today. Layer upon layer of sedimentary deposits have covered them, and they are deep underground. But there are a few places where nature and cir-cumstances have contrived to turn back the pages of the geological history book. One of the best is northern Arizona. Here the co-authors of the book are the Colorado River and the Grand Canyon. They begin their story, "Once upon a time a billion years ago near the mouth of Bright Angel Creek there lived a . . ." but we'll come to it. The earth was an island in time; it had nothing to do but exist.

The Archeozoic era came to an end. The earth was 1,800,000,000 years old and nothing much except solidifica-tion had happened yet. From its mother, the sun, it had been weaned, but it was hardly able to shift for itself. Nevertheless, it was a promising young planet.

Next came the second major geological era, the Protero-zoic. It added another six hundred and fifty million years to the youngster's age—got him out of swaddling clothes and into rompers perhaps. But as a child the earth wasn't much more interesting than he had been before. The indications of his peculiar talent, however, were present. He made a simple one-celled plant. And in the mud and slime and primordial ooze, it lived. What would this prodigy do next? All the uni-verse wondered.

Tonto Sea

B<small>Y</small> THIS time there was a no-
ticeable acceleration of development. By comparison with
times past, the tempo of evolution increased. The third great
geological era, the Paleozoic, began, and so much happened in
that era that it has been necessary to divide it into six subdivisions, or periods. The Paleozoic era, as a whole, added another three hundred and fifty million years to the life of the
earth.

Northern Arizona had been firmly based, as was most of
the rest of the world, on solid Archean rock. This was covered,
for the most part, by the rock of the second era, and this over-
lay formed the surface of Arizona when the third era began,
in turn, to cover the second. The coverage was done almost
entirely by various inundations of sea water, and the slow sedimentary deposits of sands and limes of ancient oceans gradually built new strata on top of the second-era rocks. When the
sea receded or when the land rose, the deposit remained. This
accumulation marked a "period" within the third era.

Of the six periods within the Paleozoic era, three are well
represented in the Grand Canyon's geology book, a trace of
a fourth exists, and two are missing. If we ask the earth why
he was so remiss as to leave two periods out of the record, he'll
make it clear.

The first period of the third era, however, is there. Geolo-

[6]

gists call it the Cambrian. It lasted about eighty million years and it laid down a series of mud and sand from a shallow sea and some very durable limestone as the sea became deeper.

In the Grand Canyon's open book this Cambrian deposit consisted of what geologists call locally "the Tonto group." It includes such specific classifications as Tapeats sandstone, Bright Angel shale, and Muav limestone. This invariably interests the average person not at all. But it is a moot question among the men of science, for some say that this body of water which made the sedimentary deposits should be called the Tonto Sea.

And others say it should not, that the Tonto Sea was something else altogether and that these deposits were made by the Cambrian Sea. Since they are arguing over what to call a sea which has been extinct for four hundred and eighty million years, the innocent onlooker sadly and wisely leaves the field to the men of science and stares over the rim of the canyon at the various rocks a mile below and thinks, "Golly, what a gully!"

But some time back there about four hundred and eighty million years ago the sea, by whatever name, dried up, or disappeared as the earth rose at this point, and the Cambrian period was over. The young earth was growing fast now and he added two more periods in rapid succession—the Ordovician and the Silurian. But he forgot to write them down in his Grand Canyon history book, and no matter how long he is kept after school, he still cannot recall them.

It was not really the young earth's fault, as he will explain if you give him a chance. He put the deposits of those two missing periods in the proper place all right, but a thing called erosion wore them away.

It is a very important word—erosion.

When land is under water it is going through a process of growth by sedimentation of the water that covers it; and when land is above the surface of the water it is going through a process of erosion, of being worn away by the air, wind, and water in the form of creeks, streams, or rivers that run over it. Thus the surface of the earth is never static; it is either developing or wasting away. After the now-missing Ordovician and Silurian periods had been properly deposited during the course of the earth's growth, they remained above sea level and erosion wore them away at a point called Northern Arizona. That accounts for their absence in the Grand Canyon's book.

So we see that the young earth didn't miss a trick after all. And for a like reason the fourth period of this third geological era—the Devonian—almost got away from him, too, but not quite. The Devonian lasted for fifty million years, and erosion was not able to get all of it; the earth put some evidence of it into the Grand Canyon book. The fifth and the sixth periods complete this third era; they are called the Carboniferous and the Permian. During these years—a total of about a hundred and ten million—there were several inundations. The first flood waters were those of a broad and calm sea and they deposited a pure limestone—or it may be said they built on top of the Cambrian sediments a pure limestone —for a height of five hundred and fifty feet—a solid deposition as high as the Washington Monument. This is the famous Redwall which anyone can see from almost any part of the Grand Canyon—a red belt of sheer cliff, recording what was once a huge sea.

And again comes the argument. The professional faction which declares the previous sea of the Cambrian period was not the Tonto Sea, states that the waters which deposited the Redwall were the real Tonto Sea. So . . . (There is, of course, a third faction which says *neither* was the Tonto Sea, but we won't complicate it further.)

Regardless of names, the earth was adding to its bedrock

by means of a series of inundations which built up level after level of its solid outer crust. Inside, the old heat from mother sun still persisted, and to reach a point today where water will boil because of the internal heat, it is only necessary to go down into the earth from any surface location—at the equator or at the North Pole—to a depth of 7200 feet.

The questions as to which and when was the Tonto Sea will probably never be solved. Since the name is entirely arbitrary it makes no difference at all. The name has never quite caught on with the general public anyhow. Still it is a romantic-sounding name and carries with it red sails in the sunset. It is not at all impossible that some song writer may make use of it some day. Can't you hear it?

> Carry me back to my old Tonto Sea,
> There and there only my heart wants to be.
> Dreaming of you under a Cambrian Moon,
> Five hundred million years too soon.

Why not?

But the young earth had not produced a song writer in the Paleozoic era. The Redwall was created in the Carboniferous period and the course of geologic evolution went right on. Another huge series of sediments was being formed on top of the Redwall. The sixth and last period of the third era, the Permian, was following the pattern of its predecessors. Eight hundred feet of what is called the Supai formation was deposited. After that, through the millions of years, came the Hermit shale.

On top of the Hermit shale the earth used a new trick. Instead of adding to its growth by sedimentation as it had in the past, it did the same job by means of wind-blown sand. At the Grand Canyon this is shown by a beautiful yellowish band of sandstone three hundred feet high, the second layer below the rim. Scientists call it the Coconino sandstone; they all agree on this and there is no argument about the name.

Above the Coconino sandstone, and extending to the rims, both north and south, is the last contribution of the Permian period, the gray Kaibab limestone. It has a depth of about five hundred and fifty feet. Like all limestones this was formed on an ocean bottom. You are standing on what was the floor of an ancient sea as you look over the rim into almost two billion years of geological history. But the Grand Canyon—the gash itself—is not two billion years old. That is another story.

At present we shall pause. Remember where we are. The earth was born and grew for about two billion years to the Permian period, or the end of the third major geological era. After the primordial gas cooled to liquid and the liquid cooled to a crust, the Archeozoic era began. The Proterozoic followed it. The Paleozoic, with its six subdivisions—Cambrian, Ordovician, Silurian, Devonian, Carboniferous, and Permian—came third. There are two more eras yet to account for before we bring the earth up to date, for the Permian period where we now pause ended two hundred million years before this book was written. It makes a good resting place; if you forget it or confuse it, think of it merely as the rim of the Grand Canyon today.

Meanwhile, we'll cut back to the early part of the Grand Canyon's history book and come forward again on a different theme. For the young earth's particular talent was not so much the building of rocks upon rocks. Any planet growing up can do that. The earth had its special gift. He created something rare in the universe, called life. Let's go back to Bright Angel Creek. "Once upon a time a billion years ago . . ."

Life

"... near the mouth of
Bright Angel Creek there lived an alga."

A what?

Some protophyta—some schizomycetes and thallophytes.
Well, well.

The alga wasn't alone. There were millions of him then,
and there are millions of him today. We call them, collectively,
algae. He was a single-celled primitive, microscopic, water-
growing plant, but he was alive.

Bright Angel Creek, as it is today, did not exist a billion
years ago. But the basic rocks that are there now have been
there since the cooling of the surface of the planet, the
Archean rocks that every muleback party sees as they reach
the depths of the Grand Canyon. The seas that deposited
these rocks held carbohydrates in solution. They, in turn, held
colloidal aggregates, or groups of organic cells held together
by electrical attraction. These couldn't be called life, but,
rather, charged organic matter from which life could and did
develop. The eight hundred million years of the Archeozoic
era accomplished that much and no more.

When the second geological era came in—the Proterozoic—
the organic colloids went from a liquid solution to a jelly. A
Russian scientist named Oparin, who has studied the origin of
life from sea water, considers these jellies of the primeval

oceans (he calls them coazervates) the most important step in the development of life on earth. From them came the single-celled infinitesimal first plant. It grew out of the water and slime and ooze and jelly of the second geological era and its fossilized remains may be found in the bottom of the Grand Canyon today where the rocks of the first era are met by the rocks of the second. It may safely be called the first appearance of life on earth. It lived and it died; but before it died, it split in two and one half outlived the other. So the alga became algae. As the cell division continued, the live algae continued to exist simply because their rate of dividing into two units was faster than the death rate of any one unit.

And so a billion years ago something began at Bright Angel Creek (and at other places over the primitive globe) that has never stopped, but has become more and more complex, and is going on now. At this time the new earth was not attractive as we think of it today. There were shallow seas and only rocky terrain and nothing growing except the rapidly expanding microorganisms called algae.

The earth was still cooling but so much vapor was as yet in the atmosphere that the sun was obscured by clouds. With the constant cooling process, however, the envelope of moisture condensed into oceans and the sun's rays penetrated to the surface.

The effect of the sun's rays caused the growing microorganisms to develop within themselves the vital compound chlorophyll, and this broke down the carbon dioxide in the atmosphere and allowed the plant to feed on the carbon. Thus the sun gave her creative child a great deal of encouragement. He went on with his game and soon it became more than a game. It was a serious pursuit.

As the second geological era wore on, the plant life became more complicated. And out of the same primordial jelly another one-celled being grew. It was exactly like the algae except that it wasn't a plant—it was an animal. Today we call it an amoeba—more correctly they were protozoa. After a few million years of development they became metazoa, the first animals with a digestive cavity.

Thus after the basic layer of rocks was laid down, and while the second-era rocks were being formed, the earth produced the first and simplest plant and animal life.

Evolution during the next billion years has done the rest. The Darwinian story is too well known for repetition, but as the layer upon layer of earthly crust was accumulating in Arizona, the story of life on earth was added to the story of the rocks at Grand Canyon.

The protozoa developed to an age of sponges. An age of jellyfish succeeded them in importance. Then came the third era, and the Cambrian period. In these rocks, well above Bright Angel Creek on the Tonto Platform, traces of life have been found, fossilized shells and in particular, trilobites, a crablike creature with a head and no eyes. Life in this period was entirely of a marine variety.

The next two periods, it will be remembered, are missing. Hence there are no traces in the rocks of the Grand Canyon of the creatures of Ordovician or Silurian periods—cephalopods and primitive fish. The Devonian period, the age of fishes, left its record, however, and the plates and scales of fish have been found preserved in the rocks in a few pockets of Devonian deposits just above the Cambrian's Tonto group and just below the Redwall.

The Redwall, formed in the Carboniferous period, took eighty-five million years to build. And while the sea that laid this down was not the disputed Tonto, it was rich in life. The composition of the Redwall shows a vast accumulation of plants and animal skeletons. Living things, by this time, had emerged from the sea onto land. The first amphibians began to croak; and the first of a new species, which dominated the globe at a later period, evolved from the amphibians—these were the early reptiles.

The Permian period saw the completion of the sedimentary deposits up as far as the present rim of the Grand Canyon. During this period of twenty-five million years huge ferns flourished and their fossils are found in the Hermit shale. The amphibians were the dominant species of life and their footprints are written in the Grand Canyon's book. And in the Coconino sandstone, the second strata below the rim, the tracks of twenty-seven species of animals have been found. Life was booming in the Permian period. And the period was not over. Another sea deposited the five hundred and fifty feet of Kaibab limestone, the strata of the rim. Marine life was abundant, and from it have been taken fossils of shells, corals, sponges, and even a shark's tooth.

This brings us back up to the Permian period where we paused before. So far we are just two hundred million years behind the present day.

During those two hundred million years the earth added two more geological eras—the Mesozoic and the Cenozoic. It no doubt continued to build up its surface until the Permian's last contribution, the Kaibab limestone, was covered with the deposits of Triassic, Jurassic, and Cretaceous periods of the fourth geological era. And animal and plant life continued to evolve and the age of reptiles reached its prime—with dinosaurs, pterodactyls, and ichthyosaurs.

The fifth and last geological era began only about sixty million years ago. In the Tertiary period, quadruped mammals became the dominant species. And about a million years ago—obviously very recently in view of geological time—man appeared on earth. He was a sluggish brute with a feeble brain, but he advanced to the stage of the Piltdown man, lived in a cave, and learned to use fire. A million years have brought him to what he naively calls the twentieth century.

But something strange was taking place in northern Arizona. Layer upon layer of rock, from the Archeozoic, granite and schist, had accumulated all the way up through time to the fifth geological era. Then the land rose so high at this point that it was like a huge blister on the earth's surface. When it was no longer covered by oceans, it became the victim of erosion. A great denudation took place, and nature sought to bring this upraised land into conformity with that adjacent by wearing the blister down. It completely wore away all traces of the fifth geological era, and the fourth geological era. It was as if this section of the globe were overbuilt, and nature was tearing some of it down. This great retroactive force removed everything all the way back to the end of the third geological era, the Permian period. It left a broad high plain of Kaibab limestone. Flowing across this limestone was a small trickle of water. It flowed generally toward the west. Since the fall of this stream to the sea was great, it flowed very fast. And since it flowed so fast it began to cut into the limestone. It dug itself a channel.

The blister on the globe at this point continued to rise due to internal pressure from deep within the earth. The rivulet merely flowed faster and cut its channel deeper. Even the creeks that fed it began to cut small side channels. Water erosion had begun. The little river flowed furiously on and it was fed by many tributaries. Its channel became a gulley and then a gorge and, at last, a canyon was born.

A Canyon Is Born

ALMOST every visitor to the Grand Canyon, after he has recovered from the shock of the first look, wants to know two things: "When did this happen —and what caused it?"

The answers are simple: It happened twelve million years ago; the river did it.

And the visitor, quite properly, is not satisfied. He wants to know more, and unless he has some knowledge of geology it is not likely that it will ever be very clear to him. To fill this want, the National Park Service has provided a series of lectures, and nature walks, and charts and maps and models, and a library, and a museum. They are all excellently managed, and a visitor who has never heard of geological eras and periods will begin to see daylight if he attends a few talks, and thinks about what he has seen and heard. Nature has prepared a mighty drama. At your feet is the amazing and thrilling story of the history of the earth and the life that populates it. A sensitive mind will be excited, awed, and moved. A great artist is there to perform for you if you will but take it in. You will never be quite the same again—to your advantage. Theodore Roosevelt said that the Grand Canyon was something that every American ought to see. He might have expanded the remark to include everybody on earth. Just seeing it is not quite enough; people ought to understand it. Some do; some don't. But the Park Service is making it easy for those who have a genuine desire to know more.

As we have seen, there was a time when the Grand Canyon didn't exist. This may have been twelve million years ago—or it may have been as much as a hundred million. Since man himself has been on earth only one million years, there are no witnesses as to just when the erosion process of canyon cutting began, or just when the first little trickle of water began to wear its path into the Kaibab limestone. Scientists agree, in general, that twelve to fifteen million years ago would be a fair estimate.

One thing is certain, and that is geological history. The earth built up its steady system of sedimentary deposits up to the last geological era. Then it contrived to wear away the recent strata back to the Permian period. Here it stopped the great denudation. A broad flat plain of limestone existed. A little stream ran west across the plain. Slowly the force that raised the blister on the earth at this spot raised it again. The little stream dug in deeper, and although the limestone plain sloped toward the south, the little stream refused to be thrown from its channel by this tilt. This slope of the land to the south meant, however, that most of the tributaries of the stream would come from the north. Water didn't run uphill, even twelve or fifteen million years ago.

The gash that was cut into the limestone may have been two inches deep. If so, it was probably several inches across. This was the Grand Canyon in its infancy and the little stream was the Colorado River. It is still cutting that gash deeper and wider today and will still be cutting it centuries hence. Today it is a mile deep and varies from ten to twelve miles across at the rim.

As the water erosion and canyon cutting continued, the stream began to turn backwards the pages of geological history. It cut all the way through the Kaibab limestone and hit the Coconino sandstone beneath. This meant that it was a huge canyon, for the limestone goes down into the earth for five hundred and fifty feet. It cut through the underlaying soft sandstone and into the Hermit shale. The canyon was then over eleven hundred feet deep. Two Washington Monuments, one on top of the other, would barely have reached the rim from the river. This was nothing to what was to come.

The river, at this time, must have been about as large as it is today. Wind erosion was helping to recess the side walls. A great earthquake fault, a crack which ran diagonal to the river, proved an ideal course for a side creek coming in from the north, and this side creek eroded a great gash of its own. There were other similar tributary canyons in the process of creation as century after century went around the clock. Rainfall was also helping to widen the main canyon, while in the bottom the surging river, carrying its cutting implements of sand, silt, and rocks of all sizes, went on wearing its bed deeper and deeper into the earth. The stream in the side canyon raced on to keep pace with the river. It cut equally well and it meets the river today deep in the canyon bottom. It is called Bright Angel Creek.

After about six million years of this relentless and unceasing cutting and grinding and boring and drilling, the canyon was half a mile deep and five or more miles across. It was worthy of the name Grand Canyon even then.

But the incessant water, sand, wind, and rain erosion had a long way yet to go. The whole Permian period had been exposed. And the river cut on into the Carboniferous limestone, the Redwall. It sheered the Redwall like a knife. It reached the Devonian period—the age of fishes in the Darwinian scale —and it sliced through this in a short time, that is, geologically speaking.

The Silurian period was missing and so was the Ordovician.

An earlier erosion, millions of years ago, had removed those two strata. The river never missed them; it cut on into the Cambrian rocks which had once been laid down by the erstwhile Tonto Sea. Here it was exposing to daylight rocks that had been overlaid for five hundred million years. The skeletons of the ancient trilobites with their crablike bodies were exposed along with other marine life of a mysterious ancient world.

And even deeper went the river to the very foundation of the Cambrian rocks and the meeting of the third geological era with the second. Here it turned back the pages of history to the Proterozoic, or more than a billion years.

And finally it cut down to the oldest rocks on earth, rocks that comprised the first crust when the globe was forming a solid surface and the sun had not yet penetrated the mists, rocks that held not the first live thing, but rocks that antedated even life itself. Here, then, at the canyon bottom is the stuff the earth was made of two billion years ago.

It is quite a show.

From the Permian period back to the birth of the globe is what the river and the canyon have to exhibit to anybody who makes the trip from rim to river. Nowhere else on earth can you see such a performance.

And that is not all. The whole pageant is here, not just part of it. For, to the north in Utah, an easy day's drive, is Zion National Park. If you have seen the play called "From Archeozoic to Permian," which the Grand Canyon stages, there is a sequel called the "Fourth Era," which the Painted Desert (which you pass on the way to Utah) and Zion have to present. Here you will be able to see the history of the earth from the Permian period at the Grand Canyon rim through the whole fourth era, the Mesozoic. And there is one more act after that; it is found at Bryce Canyon, also in Utah, not far

[19]

from Zion. Bryce will show you the last scene, the fifth-era formations, the Cenozoic, and that brings you right up to date. Thus it is possible for a visitor to start the day at Phantom Ranch in the canyon bottom, ascend the Bright Angel Trail to the south rim; drive via the Painted Desert to Zion National Park, and, if he hurries, pull into Bryce Canyon National Park before dark. He will have run the gamut of geological history; he will have passed through every phase of the earth's development; he will have seen the home of every species of life since the first algae swam in the primordial sea; and he will have done it all in the space of one day.

As you stand beside the roaring river at the mouth of Bright Angel Creek you wonder how much farther down into the earth this canyon will go. Where will it be in another million years? The answer is that the river will continue to cut deeper until its pitch toward sea level is sufficiently lowered so that it will no longer be a rushing torrent. At the bottom of Grand Canyon you are still more than two thousand feet above sea level. Thus the river has another two thousand feet of Archean rock to excavate before the force of gravity will be tempered and it will then be a quiet well-behaved river like the Hudson or the Delaware. Does the Archean rock extend down another two thousand feet? Yes, indeed—it extends down another thirty or forty miles, so the river will stop cutting long before it reaches the hot interior of the earth where the sun-stuff of three billion years ago is still molten.

And how long will it take to cut these next two thousand feet? Nobody knows. Since man has applied his knowledge to the phenomena at the Grand Canyon, a matter of less than a hundred years, there has been no perceptible change. Man's life span is too short to permit him to see the erosion taking place. He knows it is going on, but the movement, like that of the hour hand of his watch, is too slow for his eye to perceive.

It has been a little over four hundred years since white men first saw the Grand Canyon. And in accordance with geological time which reckons years by the hundreds of millions, man's total time on earth, to say nothing of a mere four hundred years, is not enough to count. Hence to man, change in the physiography of the Grand Canyon is negligible or nonexistent. The canyon looked very much as it does today when Columbus sailed from Spain, when Rome was founded, when Troy fell, when Hammurabi wrote the laws of Babylon. And it will still be the same two thousand years in the future. Man needn't be concerned.

II

More or Less Heroes

There's Something About
a Soldier

THE man who discovered the Grand Canyon never saw it. This paradox is not intended to be witty or fatuous, for it is technically true. It came about because of the political, military, and religious reasoning of the leaders of what was New Spain in 1540 and is Mexico today.

Hernando Cortes had landed at Vera Cruz in 1519, and by 1521 he had successfully subjugated the Aztec Empire of Montezuma. Fourteen years later, the first Viceroy of New Spain, Antonio de Mendoza, was in power at Tenochtitlan—newly renamed Mexico City—as the highest representative of his Catholic Majesty, Charles V, King of Spain; and Charles, in turn, occupied his throne as the mortal representative of God himself. Now God cannot err. Thus Charles V, God's representative on earth, could not err; and thus Antonio de Mendoza, Charles' (and God's) representative in New Spain could not err. And Mendoza declared that Captain Francisco Vasquez de Coronado discovered what we call today the Grand Canyon. According to sixteenth-century Spanish reasoning, that was exactly as if Charles V had so declared. And any statement by Charles V was divinely sanctioned. Thus, there was no doubt about it, the Grand Canyon was discovered by Captain Francisco Vasquez de Coronado, no matter if he never saw it and didn't get within two hundred miles of it.

From a point of view four hundred years removed from the culture of New Spain, some of the Spanish proprieties, amenities, manners, and morals seem unnecessarily complex, highly contradictory, and somewhat ridiculous. There were active young men in Mexico City, full of the zest for life, and they had taken on an immense job. The Spanish civilization was at full flower. To be a soldier of Spain was an admirable and coveted ambition for any young man. The Indies (the word America was hardly in use at that time) offered opportunity. To be an adventurer, a conqueror, a hero in the service of Spain was much the same in 1540 as to be a pilot or bombardier in the service of the United Nations today. It was front-line stuff and it had its thrills. We think of the Spanish *conquistadores* as doughty, rugged men of middle years, callous and cruel, brutal and bold. Instead, they were for the most part young and inexperienced, impatient and impetuous representatives of the sixteenth-century stripe of extroverts, bent on one aim—material success.

Columbus was forty years old when he sailed from Palos in 1492, and he was one of the oldest of the men who established Spain in the New World. Marcos de Niza was thirty-nine when he thought he saw the first of the fabulous Seven Cities of Cibola with streets paved with gold and studded with turquoise. Balboa was thirty-eight when he stood on a peak in Panama and discovered the Pacific Ocean. Coronado was thirty-five when he reached Mexico in search of fame and fortune. Cortes, the conqueror of the Aztec Empire, was thirty-four when he marched against Montezuma. Charles V, King of Spain, began his reign at the age of sixteen, and by the time he was twenty-seven, he ruled not only the entire New World, but had sent his armies against Rome and had

made Pope Clement VII—to him an old man of forty-nine—
his prisoner. It was a young man's world, then, now, and
always.

But it must be remembered that the heritage and condition-
ing of these men, who were to leave an indelible mark on the
Americans, were medieval. We would be in a position today
comparable to that of a Connecticut Yankee at King Arthur's
Court if we could bridge the centuries, run time backwards,
and intrude upon the political policies, mercenary machinations, and religious philosophy at the palace of the Spanish
Viceroy, Antonio de Mendoza. Things were done for reasons
seemingly illogical, but all behavior and customs were based
upon the eternal human frailties, and might seem strange to
us only because they appeared in the dress of the times. In
1941 the unaccountable Japanese had to "save face" at all
cost, in a policy born of infantilistic vanity. A similar vanity,
pride, and arrogance were characteristic of *conquistador* tem-
peraments.

In the New World of opportunity, it was inevitable that
human ambitions were bound to conflict. At the time of the
conquest, Cortes had received the lion's share of the acclaim,
and therefore Cortes had more enemies among his cohorts and
colleagues than he had among the Aztecs whom he had conquered. It was all Cortes throughout New Spain in the
1520's, and even those who pretended to be his friends were
envious and jealous. The Governor of Cuba, Velasquez, was
after his scalp for moral reasons. It is said that Cortes had
seduced the sister of Velasquez's mistress while in Cuba before his sortie to Vera Cruz. No doubt this gave Velasquez a
proper reason for damning the young soldier; and Cortes
figuratively thumbed his nose at the Governor by turning his
back on Cuba, beaching and burning his ships at Vera Cruz,
and making a conquest of the Aztecs a matter of life or death
for his army. And to add more fire to the Governor's fury,

Cortes took a new mistress in Mexico, an Indian girl named Malinche, who acted as his interpreter and was important in betraying and double-crossing the Aztec nation by playing other tribes against them. In Mexico, Cortes, by instinct, was using the Hitlerian method: divide your enemies and conquer them one by one. Thus, by abandoning one mistress and making love to another, Cortes's career flourished like the proverbial green bay tree, the Aztec Empire collapsed, New Spain rose over the ashes of Tenochtitlan, and the Fair God long feared by Montezuma had arrived.

But there were others who wished to play the same game. Velasquez, still in Cuba and furious over the fact that Cortes had outwitted him and outstripped him in the esteem of Charles V in Madrid, sent a boy to do a man's job. He commissioned one Panfilo de Narvaez to go to Mexico and place Cortes and his whole army under arrest, maintaining that Cortes had no business to conquer the Aztecs, that nobody had told him to do it, and that now he should be called on the diplomatic carpet.

Cortes, however, was enjoying the exhilaration of success. It was a bad moment to try to stop him. He simply took the unwitting Narvaez at his own game. The man and an army had come to arrest the Fair God? Very well, the Fair God arrested *him* as soon as he landed and absorbed his army into the ranks of his own. All that Velasquez's coup had done was to send Cortes unintentional reinforcements.

Thus it is easy to see that there was considerable confusion as to just who was who in New Spain. All the power plays and diplomatic jockeying took many months. Madrid was the final authority, and Charles V was too wise to let any of these scrambling soldiers of fortune get too far out of hand. He appointed a viceroy for New Spain whose authority was supreme, and in good time Antonio de Mendoza arrived. The army had done its work and now the state took over.

Meanwhile, Cortes had released Narvaez, who went bawling back to Cuba. To pacify him and his Cuban governor, Velasquez, the dextrous Charles V sent Narvaez on a conquest of Florida. If Cortes wouldn't have him in Mexico, let the fellow go shoot up Florida where, who knows, he might discover another plum.

Now all of this Spanish land-grabbing and internal strife had ramifications without end. To record it further is beside the point, but it is all strikingly significant, and the throwing of a bone to the Velasquez-Narvaez faction in the form of Florida was far more important than even Charles V realized at the time. Not that Narvaez ever amounted to anything—for he successfully wrecked his whole party off the Florida coast in 1527. The important result was that from this fiasco there survived a small group unable to get back to Cuba. This group of redoubtable Spaniards *walked* overland from Florida, around the Gulf of Mexico, on through Texas, and somehow managed to get to Mexico City by their roundabout route. It was unparalleled and amazing, this famous march of Cabeza de Vaca and his companions, and it took eight years. And here we come to an important and thrasonical figure; for with Cabeza de Vaca on this journey was a huge Negro who called himself by several names, usually Esteban de Dorantes.

Now the Viceroy, Antonio de Mendoza, had been appointed by the King in 1535, and as we have seen, the King was nobody's fool. He was a great judge of men. And Mendoza rewarded the King's confidence by loyalty and far-seeing wisdom in playing on the ambitions of the army. He never showed all his cards, and he held the *conquistadores* in check and used them to the advantage of the crown. Mendoza had all the skill of a Metternich, but he will never be as well known.

Cortes had made a trip to Spain, but he was back in 1536 looking for new worlds to conquer. The only area still un-

[29]

touched was the land to the north of New Spain—what is today the American Southwest. It was a question of who was going to be the first to have the honor and glory of conquering it and collecting a goodly share of the gold that it doubtless held.

And at this time, blown on the winds of myth, there appeared the story of the Seven Cities of Cibola. The source of this legend fades back into the limbo of wishful thinking. Probably it began conservatively, but in men's minds it caught on like a prairie fire. Somewhere to the north, the legend had it, there were seven cities paved with gold and studded with jewels beyond the farthest stretches of the imagination. And where were these wealthy seven cities? Also beyond the farthest stretches of the imagination. But nobody wanted to believe that. It was all too good not to be true; Cibola *must* exist. Then find it, Spanish soldier.

And who determined to outsmart his enemies and find it first? Hernando Cortes, of course. And the other *conquistadores* and would-be *conquistadores* said to each other, no, they weren't interested in Cibola—certainly not—and proceeded to hatch every manner of plot and to solicit all possible support to finance an expedition to find it.

Two men struck first: Cortes, and his enemy, the Viceroy Mendoza. And they used typically different methods. The extrovert Cortes followed his customary psychology. He banked everything he had on one swift move. This had worked at Vera Cruz, at Mexico City, and it should work again. Independent of the government of New Spain he assembled three ships at Acapulco on the Pacific.

He intended to lead this expedition himself up the west coast of Mexico to the thirty-fourth parallel or thereabouts, and then leave the ships and strike inland to Cibola. It was a costly venture and he put all his fortune into it. His mistress,

Malinche, had long since disappeared from his life and he was now married to a lady of Spain. To finance his expedition Cortes even had to pawn his wife's jewels.

At the last moment Cortes himself was prevented from sailing, probably on some pretext by Mendoza. So he placed his captain, Ulloa, in charge, and sent him off for Cibola on July 8, 1539. He could not fail; Cortes never failed.

Mendoza, who was only too well aware of what was going on, used a different method. He got hold of the huge Negro, Esteban, and pumped him for information, as the Negro had come down from the north on the long trek around from Florida. It is easy to visualize the interview between the crafty Mendoza and the bragging Negro, the Viceroy leading Esteban on with pointed questions. For example, had Esteban, in his glorious adventures, by some mere chance, ever heard of a place called—ah—what was that name now?

"Cibola!" exploded Esteban.

"Ah, yes, Cibola," Mendoza purred. "Unusual city—said to be fairly wealthy and lying—ah—somewhere to the north?"

"Yes, full of gold. I was there," declared Esteban.

"What!" snapped the Viceroy.

"No. I mean to say—I could go there."

"Ah," smiled the Viceroy. "Suppose you think carefully about it. To yourself. Until tomorrow."

Immediately and quietly Mendoza enlisted the services of Fray Marcos de Niza, a Franciscan who had traveled widely in the New World from Mexico to Peru and back. De Niza and Esteban were to march northward, ostensibly carrying the faith into the wilderness, and, who knows, they might get as far as Cibola! By this method the Viceroy would be spared the expense to his government of sending a huge expedition of conquest. And if Esteban could lead the priest to Cibola, they were to profess friendship for the Cibolans, estimate the wealth of the community, and return at once and report. If the report were good, Mendoza would send the full might of New Spain against Cibola at once.

Thus the year 1539 was of great importance to the future history of the American Southwest. Cortes's man, Ulloa, was sailing up the west coast; Mendoza's man, de Niza, was trudging overland, guarded by a giant Negro and the power of the cross. And both emissaries were in the field at the same time.

Ulloa had little luck. He obeyed orders and discovered a huge inland sea, together with the fact that Lower California was not an island as supposed, but an immense peninsula. Very properly he called the body of water the Sea of Cortes. Before he reached the thiry-fourth parallel, he came to the landlocked head of the sea. He tried to sail on, not knowing that he was bucking the mouth of the Colorado River, which he found a hellish place of destructive tides, and he wrote in part:

We perceived the sea to run with so great a rage into the land that it was a thing to be marveled at; and with the like fury it returned back again . . . It seemed there was an inlet whereby the sea went in and out. There were divers opinions amongst us, and some thought that some great river might be the cause thereof.

This is the first description by white men of the temperament of the Colorado River. Ulloa did not actually see the river, but he inferred its existence because of the violent tidal bores at its delta. And for the next three hundred and ninety-seven years the tempestuous violence of this stream continued to baffle men until Elwood Mead's Boulder Dam tamed it in 1936—supposedly.

Ulloa sailed south out of the Sea of Cortes, around the tip of Lower California, and up the coast. He took two of his three ships and sent the third back to Acapulco to report to Cortes that he was still looking for the thirty-fourth parallel. That was the end of Captain Ulloa; he was never heard of again. All Cortes received for his financial outlay was the honor of having his name bestowed on a landlocked sea, and even that disappeared in time. On a map printed in 1597 it is called by the unattractive name of "The California Sinus," and this, rather fortunately, was later changed to the Gulf of California.

Luck had run against Cortes at last. He left for Spain, his fortune gone, his enemies triumphant, and his wife desperately ill. It would be interesting indeed to know the thoughts of this remarkable soldier as he stood on the deck and watched the New World recede on the horizon. For he never saw it again.

Meanwhile, Mendoza's man, Fray Marcos de Niza, was having adventures of his own. On April 12, 1539, he crossed the line into what was destined to become Arizona. He had sent Esteban ahead and the two kept in contact by Indian messengers. There is a story that the Franciscan and the Negro were not of one mind. Fray Marcos was a sincere and devout man and he wished to convert the Indian bucks whenever possible. Esteban was sincere about another kind of prowess, and it is said that he wished to seduce the Indian maidens whenever possible. He decorated his giant frame with feathers and gourds and explained that he was a god. This was accepted by the Piman and Papago tribes, but Esteban overstepped when he reached the Zunis.

It is possible that the Negro really believed this pueblo was the first of the cities of Cibola. At any rate, he pranced in and affronted the Zuni people. His invulnerable godhood did not impress them, and after a brief council they decided the world would be a better place without this invader. What Esteban did in Zuni is not known, but what the Zunis did to Esteban is an historical fact. They shot a few arrows through him and discovered that what they had suspected was true, the black man was mortal after all—unless the Zuni arrows have made him immortal.

Messengers brought this shocking news back to Fray Marcos de Niza. The priest, believing the Cibolans to be belligerent in order to protect their great wealth, proceeded cautiously and looked at Zuni from a distant hill. He, too, was sure this was Cibola. Why this pueblo of mud and rock should have impressed him is difficult to say, but he reported later to Mendoza, "It has a very fine appearance . . . the best I have seen in these parts. Judging by what I could see from the height where I placed myself to observe it, the settlement is larger than the City of Mexico."

Mendoza visualized a treasure trove indeed, for hadn't the Cibolans slain poor Esteban in order to guard the secret of their wealth? And this was but one of the seven richest cities in the New World!

That was information enough for the Viceroy. He prepared two expeditions at once, one to go by sea, following the route of the Cortes-Ulloa ships, and the other to go overland, retracing the journey of Fray Marcos. And Fray Marcos, of course, would go along.

Quickly the news spread through New Spain that Cibola had been found. Hundreds of young men rushed to join the expedition. They were prepared to attack the Cibolans with fire and sword. These enemies of Spain must perish to the last man. An army of eleven hundred men was assembled in a few days. Arms and armor, guns and powder, doublets and lances, horses, cattle, and supplies were quickly made ready. Everybody was a hero before he started. All they needed was Dulcinea del Toboso to wave them on while they charged the windmills.

Mendoza approved of this spirit. His next task was to appoint one of these fine blades as the commander-in-chief and tell him to bring back the prize—the gold. He wanted a man who was not a fool, but who, on the other hand, was not too bright. Another Cortes was not desirable. Furthermore, this man must be "somebody"—an officer and a gentleman. Political and social elements had to be considered. At last the Viceroy hit upon the very man, a Spanish grandee who had been educated at the University of Salamanca and who had recently married in Mexico City the daughter of the Treasurer. (The Treasurer was said to hold his job because he was the illegitimate son of his late Catholic Majesty, King Ferdinand, grandfather of Charles V and patron of the late Christopher Columbus.) Could any man have better qualifications? Spanish customs and the cupidity of Mendoza's mind thought not. So may God save—ah—what was his name? Oh, yes, may God save Francisco Vasquez de Coronado.

This expedition, bent on loot, was so thoroughly equipped that it even had its own historian, a man named Castañeda, who wrote:

When the Viceroy saw what a noble company had come together, and the spirit and good will with which they all presented themselves, knowing the worth of these men, he would have liked very much to make every one of them captain of an army . . . but he could not do as he would have liked, and so he appointed the captains and officers because it seemed that he was so well obeyed and beloved, nobody would find fault with his arrangements.

That was thoughtful of Mendoza. And Castañeda continues:

After everybody heard who the general was, Francisco Vasquez de Coronado, the Viceroy made Don Pedro de Tovar ensign-general, the guardian and high steward of the Queen Dona Juana, our demented mistress—may she be in glory.

Mendoza wasn't missing tributes to any of the royalty, even the mentally unfit. And the historian continues:

It might be clearly seen . . . that they had on this expedition the most brilliant company ever collected in the Indies . . . but they were unfortunate in having a leader who left in New Spain estates and a pretty wife, a noble and excellent lady, which were not the least causes for what was to happen.

So this gay band of jolly fellows, consecrated to the rapine of what was a sleepy Indian village of dried-mud houses basking in sunshine, started off on their great crusade with all the excitement of a rush to the Yale Bowl for the Harvard game. They were the mighty legions of Spain, indomitable, indefatigable, and, without knowing it, ethically indecent. They were out to whip Cibola, chanting the *Santiago*, the battle cry of Spain, and it must have been quite a shock to the cheering section back home when the score turned out to be something like Cibola 74, Mexico City 0.

The ridiculous, however, is not a fair light in which to examine this expedition. The values may have been empty and the machinations Machiavellian, but it took brave and hardy men to buck the mountains and deserts of Mexico and Arizona. It must have been a long and impressive safari, colorful to the extreme, with eleven hundred soldiers and as many animals winding slowly northward over this raw land. Coronado took his leadership very seriously, and while he had no talent for this kind of thing, he was not aware of this lack. He considered himself another Cortes.

The importance of this expedition to the history of the American Southwest cannot be overestimated, for it was these soldiers who brought the first cattle and horses into a country that was to make these animals its trademark. The great-umpty-great grandparents of Kansas City beef, a million-dollar industry, were brought into a desert country by an unknow-ing soldier who came only because he hoped to take a million in gold out of it. Coronado, of course, could have only the immediate point of view. And the farther he went, the more disappointing it became. This *arida zona* looked worse with every league. He could give it nothing but a name; and those who came later contracted the name he gave it to Arizona.

At last the party came to Cibola. And here was bitter dis-appointment, for not only was the city barren of gold, but Coronado himself was wounded. And his injury occurred not in glorious battle, leading his troops against a resistant phalanx of the Cibolans—far from it, for the Cibolans offered no re-sistance at all. Coronado was hurt by falling off his horse. No sooner had he marched ingloriously into Cibola than he had to spend a month in bed. One can almost wish that this news could have been flashed to the once-valiant Cortes. It might have won a sardonic smile.

While the Spaniards tarried at "Cibola"—that is, at Zuni pueblo in New Mexico—some pertinent questions must have been fired at Fray Marcos de Niza. How the Franciscan justi-fied his former appraisal of Cibola is not known. But the priest's reputation was pretty well shattered and his name never figured again in any explorations of New Spain. He died some years later, unwept and unsung except by members of his own order, the Franciscans, in Jalapa, Mexico. But he died with a smile on his lips, for he well knew that the Cibola of his dreams was the carrying of the faith into the unknown—and this he had accomplished through his overly optimistic report to Mendoza. The church had made good use of the state.

Coronado sent his second-in-command, Pedro de Tovar, to

investigate other Indian pueblos to the northwest with the faint hope that these might be the real Cibola after all. Tovar reached Oraibi and Walpi and found the Hopis chary but friendly. Castañeda states: "It is governed like Cibola. . . . This was where they [the Spaniards] obtained information about a large river, and that several days down the river there were some people with very large bodies."

Since these men of opposite worlds could not converse in a common tongue, it is doubtful if the Castañeda version of a Hopi legend was at all clear. The Hopis believe that deep in the Grand Canyon is the orifice from which man emerged upon earth. Hence the canyon leads into the nether world and the home of the gods. This is what they were trying to tell the Spaniards, but to get that from the Shoshonean roots into a romance language with any clarity was understandably beyond Castañeda.

Tovar had been ordered to meet these people, but he had no orders to explore further. So, being a good soldier, he returned with this tale to Coronado, whereupon the incapacitated leader sent another officer to investigate the river. This man was Don Garcia Lopez de Cardenas. He took twelve men, making thirteen in all, and they went to Oraibi, picked up Hopi guides, and sought the great river.

That the men of this party of Spaniards in 1540 were the first white men to look into the Grand Canyon, there is no doubt. But the exact spot where they stood and looked into the brink is not fixed in geography. It has been identified as anywhere from Marble Canyon near Lee's Ferry to Havasu Point, twenty miles west of the present Grand Canyon village and Bright Angel Trail. Probably these extremes are wrong. Judging from Castañeda's record again, it is likely that the Hopis led the Spaniards to one of the points near Desert View. This, in some respects, is more stunning than the view from the present hotel and lodge at the head of Bright Angel

Trail, which are located deep in the side canyon caused by the Bright Angel fault. But no matter where one looks for the first time from the South Rim, he is due for a shock, and the Spaniards were no exception. Castañeda wrote conservatively and was never guilty of willful exaggeration. His matter-of-fact style is often naïve, but never mendacious. Since he was not one of the thirteen who went to the canyon, this part of his journey was written from hearsay. Pedro de Sotomayor, being a kind of undersecretary to the chronicler, went with Cardenas on this side trip, and from Sotomayor Castañeda reconstructed the junket and wrote:

. . . they came to the banks of the river, which seemed to be more than three or four leagues above the stream which flowed between them. This country was elevated and full of low twisted pines, very cold, and lying open toward the north [an excellent description of the Coconino Forest], so that, this being the warm season, nobody could live there because of the cold. They spent three days . . . looking for a passage down to the river, which looked from above as if the water was six feet across, although the Indians said it was half a league wide [there is some discrepancy here, as half a Spanish league would be one and two-fifths miles and the Colorado is actually about a hundred yards wide, or about the length of an American football gridiron]. It was impossible to descend, for after these three days Captain Melgosa and one Juan Galeras and another companion, who were the three lightest and most agile men, made an attempt to go down at the least difficult place, and went down until those who were above were unable to keep them in sight.

They returned about four o'clock in the afternoon, not having succeeded in reaching the bottom on account of the great difficulties which they found, because what seemed to be easy from above was not so, but instead very hard and difficult. They said that they had been down about a third of the way and that the river seemed very large from the place that they reached, and that from what they saw the Indians had given the width correctly.

[39]

Those who stayed above had estimated that some huge rocks on the side of the cliffs seemed to be about as tall as a man, but those who went down swore that when they reached these rocks they were bigger than the great tower at Seville.

They did not go farther up the river [meaning that the whole party did not try to follow the rim any farther] because they could not get water. Before this they had to go a league or two inland every day late in the evening in order to find water, and the guides said if they should go four days farther, it would not be possible to go on, because there was no water within three or four days, for when they [the Hopis] travel across this region themselves, they take with them women loaded with water in gourds, and bury the gourds of water along the way to use when they return and besides this, they travel in one day what it takes us two days to accomplish.

This was the Tizon River, much nearer its source than when Melchior Diaz and his company crossed it.

The last casual sentence needs some explanation. It should be remembered that the meticulous Mendoza never did anything by halves. He sent not only a land expedition to conquer Cibola, but also one by sea. It was supposed in 1540 that both routes would run parallel, and in order to ease the land burden, many supplies were sent by boat under the command of Hernando de Alarcón up the west coast. The two expeditions were supposed to keep in contact by overland messengers.

Because the geography of North America was so little understood in 1540, Mendoza did not know that Coronado would be marching due north, and that Alarcón would be following a north-northwest coastline. The farther they went, the greater became the distance between them.

Alarcón, nevertheless, did not intend to fail the Viceroy. When he reached the head of the Sea of Cortes, which had frightened Ulloa, he kept on and fought his way up the Colorado River. The current was too strong for him to sail against, so his crews (he had three ships) were obliged to tow the boats from the bank. The naked Cocopah Indians looked on in amazement, but Alarcón knew that Coronado was counting on the supplies on shipboard and he dared not fall back at the first adversity.

Alarcón was not at all sure of Cocopah friendship, but a clever ruse outwitted the natives. He discovered that they worshiped the sun. Promptly he made them understand that he had come from the sun and was the god of it. It was fast thinking and the Cocopahs believed him. After that they quarreled for the honor of towing the Sun God upstream in his water chariot, and the Spanish crews relaxed on the decks while the red men sweated.

It is not established how far up the Colorado the Cocopahs pulled the Spaniards, but it is certain from Alarcón's records that he ascended beyond the site of the present city of Yuma and even beyond the mouth of the Gila. And nowhere did he hear any news of Coronado, who was in New Mexico more than four hundred miles to the east. The two expeditions never made contact, though they came surprisingly close to it.

Coronado sent another side party overland to find Alarcón, and a man named Melchior Diaz was in charge of this. At Alarcón's farthest penetration upstream, he had a large cross constructed and gave the natives many small crosses made of sticks and parchment. He called the Colorado *el Rio de Buena Guia* (River of Good Guidance) in honor of the motto on Viceroy Mendoza's coat of arms. Then he sailed south again and gave up as a bad job any further effort to act as a source of supply for Coronado.

He had been gone about a month when the Melchior Diaz party found the river and discovered Indians wearing crosses made of sticks and parchment. Thus Diaz learned that Alarcón had come and gone. Diaz marched up and down the river and called it *Rio del Tizon* when he observed natives warming themselves with a firebrand. Diaz did not find the large cross, but the fact that the two parties came as close as they did to actual contact was remarkable in itself. While exploring the adjacent desert country and fighting the hostile Mojaves, Diaz was mortally wounded, and he died before he could get back to report to Coronado. When his men returned to Cibola with this news, it was one more blow for the gentleman from Salamanca, who was now heartily sick of the whole thing.

Castañeda's narrative was written in full at a later date. The Diaz men had returned, and this is why he says that the stream in the bottom of the Grand Canyon was the Tizon River. He knew that Diaz had called it this, but he did not know that Alarcón had previously given it another name.

Coronado was at last able to travel again. So far everything had been a failure. De Niza was a palpable liar; Cibola was made of mud; Tovar found the Hopi villages to be the same; Cardenas found the river so inaccessible that it was useless; Diaz had lost his life in a futile effort to meet Alarcón; and not an ounce of gold had been found anywhere.

More rumors came from beyond the blue New Mexican horizon—rumors of a great golden city in a place called Quivira. Coronado heaved a long sigh and the eleven hundred, less a few casualties, marched again.

For two years the Spaniards traveled and searched and hoped—and none of the hopes were realized. They worked their way over the plains as far east as Kansas—and it was all, to them, a vast, empty, worthless, God-forsaken country. In 1542 they straggled back to Mexico City. Some left their bones in the American Southwest; some were wounded from skirmishes with the warlike Apaches and Comanches; some were ill; and all were discouraged and exhausted. Coronado, erstwhile emulator of Cortes, was disgraced and discarded. No proud welcome awaited him, and his pretty wife had lost her heart to another man.

Nothing succeeded with Viceroy Mendoza except success. He had no time for dolts and fools. He was so disgusted that he would not even see the gentleman from Salamanca. Coronado had been given every chance to find Cibola and he had failed. The fault was entirely Coronado's. In a report on the expedition, Mendoza had credited all discoveries to the leader, regardless of who saw the prize first. Since Coronado had explored for two years and discovered nothing, he got credit for that, too. About all that the Viceroy could glean that this piffling picaroon had done was to discover a big hole in the ground. Well, it was too bad his men hadn't carried him all the way from Zuni, bed and all, and tossed him into this *Canyon grande*. And with that the Viceroy looked around to find a new hero.

Coronado died a broken man at the age of forty-nine. He never understood that he had opened a vast new area, rich in natural resources beyond estimation. He had none of the fight and fire of Cortes; he humbly accepted his failure. He never knew how to tell a viceroy to go to hell. And if he had known, it wouldn't have helped. For Cortes had known full well how to do that, and he was a broken man, too.

This pattern is not uncommon with the soldiers who pioneered America, and it is especially true for the explorers of the American Southwest. It was a stark and terrible country, and it was greater than any single man. The land was there when they came and there when they left. It left its mark on its invaders, but hundreds of years passed before the invaders could leave their mark on it.

The silence at the abysmal brink of the Grand Canyon was not broken again by white men for two hundred and thirty-six years. This awful and gorgeous maw was a hostile force that the soldier could not conquer or even understand. He preferred not to think of it and the very existence of the Grand Canyon was ignored and forgotten. The Spanish soldier knew how to attack an enemy, but before the Grand Canyon country he was as powerless as an infant. Its deep and mysterious silence was the sound for retreat.

The Little Man and the Big Cross

WHITE men (and women) have been coming to the Grand Canyon and peering over the rim for various reasons for more than four hundred years. The approach can be divided into five stages, and the visitors fall into five classifications.

The first were the Spanish conquistadors, a relatively small group numbering only thirteen men. They looked, they marveled, they condemned, and they went away. The canyon did not interest them for they were looking for gold. Following the soldier, as is normal in the course of history, came the priests. This second group of visitors was again Spanish, and throughout the Southwest the Franciscans and the Jesuits followed their consciences and carried their faith into the more or less unknown. Three of these men reached the Grand Canyon country in 1776 and their names are well known to students of the region. And they, too, looked, marveled, condemned only slightly, and went away. The canyon did not interest them for they were looking for souls. The third group consisted of Americans. They were trappers, scouts, frontiersmen, and they came from the 1820's to the 1850's. They looked, marveled, condemned hardly at all, and went away. The canyon did not interest them for they were looking for furs, hides, and pelts. The fourth group was made up of American explorers and scientists and artists who came to the area because of the area itself. They looked, marveled, condemned not at all, and some of them stayed. The canyon interested them especially for they had come to study it. Their era began about 1858 and it is still going on today. This is the first group whose individuals can be numbered in hundreds, perhaps thousands. The fifth group was primarily American although it has included a sprinkling of every nationality on earth. These were and are the tourists. They come and look and marvel and make remarks and go away. The canyon interests them for they are seeking entertainment and escape, and this group can be numbered in the millions.

When Spanish exploration from 1540 to the late seventeenth century ceased to have a military significance it became the province of the church. Men such as Padre Eusebio Kino, a Jesuit, traveled widely over the Southwest. Kino was a tireless and zealous man who founded many missions in Sonora, Arizona, and California. He was, incidentally, an Austrian, and few realize that any man born in Vienna had much to do with Southwestern history. His name was Kuhn, sometimes spelled Kuhne, and its Spanish variation is either Quino or Kino. His base of operations was the Mission of Dolores which he founded in 1687 in the Mexican state of Sonora, and he crusaded vigorously over the raw and dangerous desert country for twenty-five years. His type of expedition, either alone or with acolytes or Indian servants, was called an *entrada,* a name which seems more correctly descriptive when not translated. He never saw the Grand Canyon, but he was familiar with the Colorado River for a long distance up from the Gulf of California, and his missionary work led the way for other priests to follow.

The Colorado River was still receiving names at this time. Ulloa had failed to name it in 1539 only because he did not actually see it from his cockleshell ship tossed about near its mouth. Alarcón called it the River of Good Guidance in 1540; Diaz called it the Firebrand River the same year; Juan de Oñate, who had explored the Rio Grande Valley before coming farther west, called it the River of Good Hope in 1604; and Kino called it the River of the Martyrs in 1702.

None of them stuck, and it remained for Kino's most distinguished successor, Padre Francisco Tomas Garces, to give it a fifth and final name in 1775. He called it Colorado because it was. The word may be translated as "colorful" and also as "reddish." The river is both and Garces's name has held.

In 1767, long after Kino's death, the Jesuits were expelled from all parts of the Spanish dominions and their mission property was taken over by the crown. The Viceroy of Mexico asked the Franciscan College at Queretaro for priests to continue the missionary work in Sonora and Pimeria Alta (Arizona). Fourteen young men responded. Among them was Francisco Tomas Garces. He reached the Mission San Xavier del Bac near Tucson which still stands today in the Arizona sun, an architectural achievement, and a monument to the devotion of Jesuits and Franciscans alike, to say nothing of Papago Indian labor which made the edifice possible.

Beginning in June, 1768, Garces made five great *entradas*, traveling widely from southern Arizona to the Colorado River, up and down its banks, and on to the Mission San Gabriel near Los Angeles, California—except that in those days there was no Los Angeles. His fifth and final journey was the greatest of them all. It is said that his travels covered twenty-five hundred miles, and that he carried the cross to twenty-five thousand Indians. He was a quiet, soft-spoken, simple little man who lived only to serve what he considered the greatest truth on earth, love for his fellow man.

He traveled alone much of the time, and occasionally he enlisted Indians to guide him from tribe to tribe. Sometimes he walked; sometimes he rode a mule. It was impossible for him to carry much more than the clothes on his back and most of the time he had to depend upon native food. Padre Pedro Font, a less hardy Franciscan brother, comments on Garces: "He seems just like an Indian himself . . . and though the food of the Indians is as nasty and disgusting as their dirty selves, the padre eats it with great gusto." Never in these journeys did Garces ever think of going armed. He had strength only for greater ammunition than bullets—his faith, his cross, his love.

Garces' fifth *entrada* began in the summer of 1776 and he worked upstream from the present site of Yuma, Arizona, and visited the Mojave Indians near what is now Needles, California. He then decided to move easterly across northern Arizona and travel as far as the Hopi settlement of Oraibi. This objective was important to him because the priests from Santa Fe, and other settlements in the Rio Grande Valley, had not done too well with the Hopi people. Almost a hundred years previously, 1680, to be exact, the Hopis had risen in an outburst of sporadic violence and killed the few priests and soldiers who had come among them. This was not altogether a blot on the Hopis' usually peaceful record. The Spaniards had come professing to bring them salvation which they did not want (the Hopis were, and are still, among the most advanced Indians of North America) and had proved instead to be emissaries of the flesh and the devil when soldiers seduced a number of the Hopi girls. The Hopis put a quick stop to this, but they did it in their own aboriginal way. They decided the only good Spaniard was a dead Spaniard. Garces knew of this and considered it most regrettable, and with his never-failing courage and zeal, he determined to visit the Hopi and convince them that not all white men were bad men, and that the teaching of Christ was intended for all.

On his way all alone, the priest met a number of Walapai Indians and they volunteered to act as guides and take him to another tribe hidden away in the fastness of a deep canyon, a tribe which no white man had ever seen. Moreover, this unknown canyon was on the trail that would eventually lead to Oraibi. Garces was delighted. He kept a careful record of this remarkable trip and in 1900 it was meticulously translated by Dr. Elliott Coues and published under the title of *On The Trail of a Spanish Pioneer*. And thus it is from the priest's own diary that his itinerary can be traced and his visit to the Land of the Sky Blue Water enjoyed in detail.

About thirty-five miles west of what is today Grand Canyon village on the South Rim, a road leads to the head of the Topocoba Trail. From here it is another fourteen miles down the precipitous trail by mule or Indian pony to Havasu Creek in Cataract Canyon where live the Havasupai Indians. This is one of the most remote and inaccessible tribes in America. In some respects it represents a native culture that has maintained its characteristics and resisted white influence more than that of any other tribe. And from another point of view it has absorbed a great number of the white man's institutions. The Havasupais remained a tiny ethnological group sufficient unto themselves because they were so very hard to reach. Nature was their retreat, and for the majority of them, year after year and century after century, their universe was bounded by the walls of the giant fissure in which they lived. In a later section of this book we shall visit the Havasupais and examine the Land of the Sky Blue Water from a contemporary point of view. Many of their characteristics today are identical with those of 1776 when a lone priest was approaching their little world and they were about to see a white man for the first time.

The thirteen English colonies had not yet declared their independence from George III when Padre Garces reached the Land of the Sky Blue Water. The Walapai Indians lived in the high country above the eroded gashes and canyons and they were friendly with the Havasupais. It was the Walapai (the Pine-Tree People) who led Garces over the difficult terrain which approaches Havasu Creek and Cataract Canyon from the southwest. This is known as the Walapai Trail and it is just as difficult today as it was in 1776—and so is the Topocoba by which means Garces left.

The Havasupais are extremely friendly people. They smile at a stranger and bid him, "*Tchew Ko-mew* [Hello, how are you]." Wars and torture, and rites of blood and sacrifice, are foreign to their nature. Life is beautiful and peaceful to the Havasupai in his rich little canyon surrounded by huge red walls. He thinks he is on earth to be happy—and so he is. He thinks that way today, and he was thinking that way in 1776. Garces's diary gives an excellent account of his visit and some quotations from the original are essential for a measure of Garces himself.

June 20, 1776. I went five leagues east, two northeast, and three north, the last four of these over very bad ground through some caxones [canyons] the most profound, though all were well grassed with plenty of trees. I arrived at a rancheria [any agricultural settlement was so-called by Garces] which is on the *Rio Jabesua* [*Jabesua* is pronounced almost exactly like Havasu and is the same word in Spanish version] . . . and in order to reach this place I traversed a strait. This extends about three-quarters [of a league]; on one side is a very lofty cliff, and on the other a horrible abyss. This difficult road passed there presented itself another and worse one, which obliged us to leave, I my mule and they [the Walapais] their horses, in order that we might climb down a ladder of wood.

All the soil of these caxones is red; there is in them much mezcal; there are some cows and horses, most of which are branded, and some have several such marks: I recognized none of them, but of a single one I doubted whether it were not of the mission San Ignacio. . . .

Probably it was not, as this mission was far south in Sonora, Mexico. But it is interesting to note that even on this labor of love, Garces was not without an eye for cattle stolen from the Franciscan missions. He continues:

I asked these Indians, as I had done before in other rancherias, whence did they procure these horses and cows; and they replied, from the Moqui [another name for the Hopi] where there are many ill-gotten cattle and horses.

I arrived at the place of our stopping for the night, [probably at the widest, and hence most farmed, spot in Cataract Canyon; it is the site of a school and resident agent's house today] and as I saw the Jabesua Indians well supplied with some pieces of red cloth, I suspected therefrom that they might be some of the Apaches who harass these provinces. My suspicion increased when the women came, and among them some whiter than is the rule in other nations. [Garces knew that if these people had Apache blood his life might be in danger.] In spite of this I had no fear, seeing all well content at my arrival, and that they embraced with pleasure the peace proposed with their inveterate enemies, the Jamajabs [Pronounced Hamahabs and meaning the Mojaves. These people occasionally raided the Havasupais and the Havasupais were naturally pleased that Garces suggested intertribal peace] . . . also did I propose to them to cultivate pleasant relations with the padres and the Spaniards who would soon come to live on the Rio Colorado.

So pleasing was the insistency with which they urged me to remain in this rancheria that as I found myself constrained perforce in this place, I had to remain five days; during which they waited upon me and regaled me with flesh of deer and of cow, with maize, beans, *quelites*, and mezcal, with all of which they were well provided. They also eat a berry of the juniper, a tree which is very abundant in these lands. I had much complacency to see that as soon as it was dawn each married man with his wife and grown sons went forth to till his fields, taking the necessary implements, as hatchets and hoes, all of which they procure from the Moqui.

These people go decently clothed, and are very fond of any red cloth of Castilla which comes from New Mexico. That there are here women so white, I saw one who looked like a Spaniard. I attribute it to the situation of the place wherein they live; for this is so deep that it is ten o'clock in the day when the sun begins to shine. [The sun comes up as usual, but Garces means that the side canyon of the Grand Canyon is so deep at this point that it is ten a.m. before the direct rays come over the rim.] Whithersoever I have gone I have seen no situation more strong and secure by nature.

These families do not exceed thirty-four in number [allowing seven members to the average Havasupai family, they totalled two hundred and thirty-eight in 1776 which has been a fairly constant level of population and just about all that the arable land will feed. They numbered two hundred and fourteen in 1943 according to the agent's census]. Close by runs the Rio Jabesua, which arises in the labyrinth of caxones there are in every direction; the course it here takes is to the northwest and north, and at a little distance it falls into the Rio Colorado. This [Havasu Creek and *not* the Colorado] is a river of middling size but very rapid, and the Jabesuas utilize it well with many dams and ditches.

During his five-day visit Garces explained Christianity to two hundred and thirty-eight people who had never heard of it and who had generally supposed that they and a few nearby tribes were the only people on earth. After giving it a little thought they could see no sense to the odd and meaningless stories of Christian faith. They smiled and said yes, but inwardly they felt a bit sorry for this confused stranger who obviously had no peace of mind such as they had and who had to go through life an unfortunate victim of obsession, traveling from place to place talking nonsense. They tried to be very kind. And thus the first Christian message to penetrate the Grand Canyon country met not with rebuff, but with polite sympathy. With crucifixions and torture and mobs and confusion and kings and rabble and miracles and ascensions—it must be a dreadful world this poor white man came from.

Why didn't he forego it all and stay here by the laughing blue water and the majestic red cliffs and the fertile green fields forever? There was plenty for all and the warm sun shone every day and the nights were cool and everybody was happy. Why go?

Padre Garces insisted that he had to go on. He had a mission to perform. There were others who needed to hear his stories. He could not tarry in one place long. He had demands upon himself.

The Havasupais smiled among themselves. One of them thought he had the answer. Perhaps it was that the white man had to go on because he wanted a wife.

The Franciscan protested.

But they would be happy to provide him a girl. Every man had a wife, and while it was not customary for Havasupai girls to marry outside the tribe, they could make an exception in this case since he was obviously a good and well-meaning man, and if he were to take a Havasupai girl his strange madness and hallucinations about crosses might pass. And, in time, he could marry her. It was always done that way. And, who knows, he might even get to be a medicine man.

Thus the Franciscan found himself a tiny island of Christian morality entirely surrounded by people of pagan morality. He decided there was much work to be done before he could ever bring the Havasupais to Jesus—so much, in fact, that to undertake the teaching would preclude his ever getting to his destination, Oraibi, and the Hopi people. Putting these children of ignorance aside with the mental reservation that here was a great field for somebody—but somebody else—Garces blessed them all for their innate goodness and said a prayer for their ungodly sins and bade them good-bye. They smilingly watched him go, and their medicine man said a prayer that the poor white man's derangements might be healed. And they never saw each other again.

Garces' diary omits details between June 20 and June 25, the time of his five-day visit, but on this latter date he writes soberly:

I set forth accompanied by five Indians and traveled south and east, now on horseback, now on foot, but in both these ways with great exertion, and halted on the slope of the sierra at a scanty *aguage* [probably Topocoba Spring]. In the afternoon I finished the most difficult part of it [the ascent]. They cause horror, those precipices—and thereafter traveling north over good ground with much grass, and many junipers and pines and other trees among which I went about three leagues, I arrived at a rancheria which appertains to the Jabesua, whither had come some of this nation to gather the first of the juniper. The principal Indian offered himself to accompany me next day.

It is evident that Garces had ascended the Topocoba Trail but he does not say what happened to his mule which was left at the head of the ladder leading down the Walapai Trail. It is probable that a Walapai guide had brought it around the rim country to the head of the Topocoba Trail, for as thrifty and as frugal a man as Garces could not have abandoned a good mule. Apparently he spent the night at what is now Pasture Wash, and in the morning set out with his one remaining Havasupai guide. "June 26, 1776. I traveled four leagues southeast, and south. And turning to the east halted at the sight of the most profound caxones which ever onward continue, and within these flows the Rio Colorado."

Garces was standing on the South Rim of the Grand Canyon. He was the first white man to look into the abyss since Cardenas and his men had stood beside it in amazement in 1540.

"There is seen a very great sierra, which in the distance looks blue," he wrote, and since he does not say where this mountain is, it could have been Navajo Mountain a hundred miles to the northeast, or it could have been the Kaibab Plateau to the north across the canyon proper. He is specific, however, about the topography in general.

And there runs from southeast to northwest a pass, open to the very base, as if the sierra were cut artificially to give entrance to the Rio Colorado into these lands. I named this singular pass *Puerto de Bucareli* [Bucareli was Viceroy of Mexico in 1776], and though to all appearances it would not seem to be very great, the difficulty of reaching thereunto, I considered this to be impossible in consequence of the difficult caxones which intervened.

Garces was standing at a spot where the Grand Canyon lay at his feet to the north, and to the northeast he was looking straight up the gash cut by Marble Canyon. So very definitely he was somewhere between what is now Grand Canyon village and Grandview Point. "Also were there seen on the north some smokes, which my companions said were those of the Indians whom they name Payuches, who live on the other side of the river."

They do indeed. For that was smoke of a Paiute camp on the Kaibab Plateau, not only "on the other side of the river" but on the other side of a gorge a mile deep and ten miles across. "I am astonished at the roughness of this country and at the barrier which nature has fixed therein."

And cogitating upon the strange ways of God, of nature, of man, the little priest traveled on, following the general direction of the South Rim and fixing in his mind and recording in his diary the landmarks of the region. He had a quick sense of contour and he understood the country very well indeed as it unfolded its design before him. He met other Indians and together they journeyed on to Oraibi, the march taking five days.

It would be pleasant to record that this well-meaning little man was well received by the Hopis, but he was not. It would be even more pleasant to record that he spent the rest of his days in the teaching of Christianity to the red men and that he died satisfied and happy, knowing that he had served his God well on earth. And neither did this happen. Garces was destined for a tragic death.

The Hopis mistrusted him in 1776. He arrived at Oraibi on the second of July, and the chiefs would not permit him to enter the houses of the pueblo. He was forced to camp outside. The people would have nothing to do with him, although they were curious enough to stare while he cooked his own supper. On the third of July conditions were no better. Garces hoped to win the Hopis over to an amicable relationship, but they steadfastly refused to be friends. On the fourth of July the chiefs and dignitaries dressed up in feathers and paint, marched to Garces' camp outside the town, and commanded him to leave. He held up his crucifix and tried to explain that he had come to save their souls. They thought it was bad medicine and some were sullen and others were openly belligerent. Garces realized that his continued presence would only aggravate these people further, and so he sadly and wearily collected his scant supplies, packed them on his faithful mule, and slowly rode away. His heart was torn at seeing so many poor Indians going straight to hell for the lack of only three drops of water which he would gladly sprinkle over them if only they would let him do it. He blamed himself, not the Hopis—and in his prayers he asked God to forgive him his failure for surely he must not be pure in heart or he would have won these people to the faith.

In 1779 he established the Mission Purisima Concepcion on a hill overlooking the Colorado River on the California side across from the present city of Yuma. Here his work among the Yuman Indians was successful, and another mission called San Pedro y San Pablo was built eight miles downstream. Garces labored and lived happily for three years, and doubtless bestowed upon the Yuman Indians with loving care the saving three drops of water.

Stupid and tyrannical government on the part of Spanish officials caused the Yuman tribe to revolt in 1781. They murdered every Spaniard—cleric, layman, and soldier—and took the women prisoners. Against the better judgment of the chief of the tribe, the warriors clubbed Garces to death while the little man clung loyally to the cross. And all too late the Yumans realized that they had martyred their best friend and the only white man who had ever understood them. It is said that the Yuman chief, Captain Palma, who had ordered Garces alone to be spared, wept over his body. Normally this story might be discredited, but, when one remembers Garces and his unselfish labors and the doglike devotion of the Yuman chief to him, it is probably true.

Thus died Francisco Tomas Garces. His career is important in Southwestern history, for not only was he the first white man to travel along the rim of the Grand Canyon and to describe it accurately in writing, but he gave a lasting name to the river that created the canyon, and he spent the remainder of his life spreading love and kindness from his Mission Purisima Concepcion within sight of the stream.

"Soul" is a difficult word because it is used all too easily. It may be defined, however, as the non-corporeal nature of man, and again, as the moral and emotional nature as distinguished from the purely intellectual and scientific, which, however, it includes. To say of anybody or anything that he or it has a great soul, is attaching to it something transcendental, or *a priori* according to Immanuel Kant. Nevertheless, the word "soul" is used glibly and is often semantically foggy. In spite of this risk it can truthfully be said that Francisco Tomas Garces was a little man with a great soul. The details that he preached and the methods that he used and his personal beliefs have nothing to do with this conclusion. Had he been born a Hindu or a Jew he would have preached differently, but he still would have had a great soul.

And it is poetically just that this little corporeal being who reflected a great soul should have trudged his way overland through an unknown wilderness to look upon a work of nature which, in its own way, also reflects a great soul. Padre Garces and the Grand Canyon had to meet. He was indeed a kind of Bright Angel, and the spiritual zeal of the man has much in common with the awesome impact and the angelic power of the canyon. The little man who worshiped the big cross never stood before a man-made altar which could compare with his "most profound caxones which ever onward continue." He may not have reasoned thus. It was a union in spirit.

At the site of the Mission Purisima Concepcion today there is a government agency and Indian school for the Yumans. A statue of Padre Garces stands there looking serenely out over the Colorado River. It will probably stand there as long as man is on earth. And the river will continue to surge through the Grand Canyon a few hundred miles upstream and come rolling down past the statue as long as man is on earth. Soul has nothing to do with space and time.

Escalante and Dominguez

J UST what, and where, is the geographical point known by the romantic name of El Vado de los Padres, or the Crossing of the Fathers? Few Americans have ever heard of it, and fewer still have ever seen it. And fewer still can say who the "fathers" were and what it is they crossed and when and why.

Yet this point marks one of the important monuments in the exploration and winning of the West. A vanguard, or perhaps, in contemporary vernacular, "a task force," made contact with the great unknown. Adventure, excitement, exploration, physical hazards of all kinds; uncertainty, suffering, daily risks, and the strain on human nerves to the breaking point—all were endured by a party of ten men who have not been forgotten by American history books, but who, ironically enough, were never even remembered in the first place.

There are several reasons for this, and the first is that the expedition in question set out from Santa Fe, New Mexico, on July 29, 1776. Now July 4, 1776, was a great day in America and it is fittingly remembered. But there was not a solitary citizen of the infant United States who had ever heard of Don Bernardo de Miera y Pacheco. The nation that was to become the United States of America possessed thirteen Atlantic seaboard colonies and its influence had hardly been felt west of the Appalachian chain and certainly not west of the Mississippi. As that influence did spread west, however, it carried on its successive waves the heroes of the Westward Movement in America. Today everybody can identify Lewis and Clark; every schoolboy wishes he could have marched with Daniel Boone; and many a youngster has played at riding the plains with Kit Carson and Buffalo Bill. But I doubt if any ten-year-olds have ever begun a game by saying, "I'll be Escalante and you be Dominguez."

The West, which is supposed to be the youngest part of the United States, is in many respects the oldest. There were permanent Indian villages in Arizona before Columbus was born, and these villages exist today. Oraibi and Walpi are but two examples; Zuni in New Mexico is another. And the Spanish city of Santa Fe was a hundred and seventy-one years old in 1776. The white man has been on the Eastern seaboard well over three hundred years, but he has been in the American Southwest for more than four hundred.

But the Eastern culture has washed over the Western. The Spanish outposts have become anglicized and many of the Spanish heroes have faded in time—de Niza, Melchior Diaz, Oñate, Ulloa, Garces, Kino are names pertaining to the Southwest, but, beyond that generality, identification is none too specific in the American mind today. And this is perfectly understandable, for the incoming civilization from the East brought its own heroes, while the records of the Spaniards exist today in the libraries of Mexico and in the archives of the *Deposito de la Guerra* in Madrid.

Nothing was known of the area between Santa Fe in the upper Rio Grande Valley and Monterey on the Pacific Ocean in California in 1776. No overland journey had been made between the two Spanish cities and a vast region totally unexplored lay between them. The Governor of New Mexico was interested in closing this gap and he encouraged an expedition. Ten men were selected to make up the party and the

most important of the ten, the leader, was a citizen of Santa
Fe, Don Bernardo de Miera y Pacheco. That this journey into
the wilderness should have been known as the de Miera expedition would seem inevitable and so it was. Yet historians
look blank when you mention it today. And finally a light
dawns and they say, "Oh, you mean Escalante and Dominguez—yes, very important—but I don't know just what it accomplished—if anything. Do you?"

Like most other ventures, the de Miera expedition came
into existence for business purposes. Its members went along
for various reasons depending upon their individual ambitions,
but chiefly for prestige, the claiming of new lands, the establishment of trade routes, financial benefits, and exploitation in general. The Governor of New Mexico urged de
Miera to consider the possibilities of colonizing the huge area
which comprised what is now a large part of New Mexico,
Arizona, Colorado, and all of Utah and Nevada. No small
job. And no white man had ever seen the land through which
the projected route was to go. All they knew was that if they
continued northwesterly and westerly long enough they
should come out at Monterey in California or Somewhere.

It turned out to be only Somewhere.

Under de Miera, the next most important member was a
Spanish priest, Padre Franco Atanacio Dominguez. And third
in importance came another priest, Padre Silvestre Velez de
Escalante. The two fathers were not so much interested in the
extension of trade and commerce as they were in the bringing
of the faith into the wilderness. It was known that there were
aborigines in this hinterland of New Spain. Here was a country that did not yet know the cross. Onward!

After the leader, and the priests, came the practical men of
business. In importance they ranked in this order:

4. Juan Pedro Cisneros, the mayor of Zuni
5. Joaquin Lain of Santa Fe

6. Lorenzo de Olivares of El Paso
7. Juan de Aguilar of Bernalillo
8. Simon Luzero, a servant of Lain
9. Andres Muniz
10. Antonio Muniz.

The last two were not shareholders in the expedition but were merely employed as guides. That they had never seen the land over which they were to guide was understood by all; they were really servants of the expedition, but they had previously penetrated into northwestern New Mexico and could "guide" for the first week or two. On July 29, 1776, this party set forth.

Nobody heard anything more of them for over six months. Then, on January first, 1777, they arrived back in Santa Fe, coming in from a totally different direction from that in which they had started. They had traveled sixteen hundred miles on direct route and over two thousand counting side trips.

Had they been to Monterey?

No.

Had they found any new trade routes?

No.

Had they made any new converts?

No.

Had they found any new natives to exploit?

No.

Had they seen any mineral wealth—gold perhaps?

No.

Had they located the sites for any new colonies?

No.

Well, what in the name of the Blessed Sacrament had they been doing all this time?

Walking.

By January second, 1777, a reaction to this expedition had taken place in the public consciousness of the city of Santa

Fe. It had been a failure, a complete and unmitigated failure. Those who had backed the expedition had wasted their money. This fiasco had cost plenty and accomplished nothing. The attitude was one that in later years was taken toward a man who proved he could sit on a flagpole for a week, or a month. It was simply, "So what?" Nobody was going to finance another trek into that unproductive wilderness. The high tide of Spanish infiltration into North America had been reached, and the last wave had washed up onto a barren littoral. Let New Spain consolidate its vast domain, but let it expand its frontiers no farther. And with the de Miera expedition the Spanish advance northward from Mexico into the American West came to an end. Historically, this is important. For had the power of New Spain continued to advance northward and westward until it held by force of physical possession all of Colorado, Utah, and Nevada, and had it pushed on and claimed Wyoming and Idaho, the inevitable clash between such an empire and the westward-moving forces of the United States would have written another chapter to the so-called "Mexican War."

Since the de Miera expedition aroused no enthusiasm in Santa Fe in 1777, it is interesting to examine it in more detail and find out what was wrong, for oddly enough it was the first appraisal of one of the richest areas on earth.

The trip had not been ill prepared or impetuously planned. The forgotten de Miera probably left no account of his travels, but the third member of the party, Escalante, kept a journal and recorded many facts in careful detail.

It is also interesting, in passing, to note the rise in importance (if the expedition has any claim to importance at all, and in the long view it truly has) of this man Escalante. He was no doubt outranked by Dominguez as Dominguez's name always comes first in the records after de Miera. But Escalante is a euphonious name. It is somehow more attrac-

tive to the Anglo-Saxon ear and eye than either de Miera or
Dominguez. Semi-illiterate men recalled it readily. One of
Major Powell's boatmen, who battled their way down the
treacherous Colorado River in 1869, refers, in a letter, to the
name as "Eskalanty." Posterity has selected it from the list of
ten who made up the trip as the name to survive, and there
are students of the American West who take it for granted
that the whole expedition was made at Escalante's instigation
and that he was the leader. This matters little, but the tricks
played by a name and a hundred and fifty years or more help
to set the supposed course of history.

The party left Santa Fe with pack animals and horses and
moved northwest through the wild but known terrain of New
Mexico, crossed into Colorado, and passed through the valley
in which Durango is now located. Keeping generally northward they saw much of western Colorado and reached the
site of Delta by September first. Slowly they worked north
and west and entered Utah at or near the White River. Here
in the great unknown they discovered what later arrivals
called the Green River, coming down from Wyoming, and
they named this the San Buenaventura. With this party the
Utah wilderness resounded to the tread of horses' hoofs for
the first time, and to this day there are still huge sections of
Utah which can be visited by foot or by horseback only. The
ruggedness of this state has long proven a barrier to man's
efforts, and as for the important Crossing of the Fathers on
the violent Colorado in Southern Utah, you will have to go
by foot or horseback if you wish to see it even now, unless, of
course, you fly.

On September 13, the party reached its northernmost point
and the banners of New Spain were only fifty miles from
what eventually became the very un-Spanish state of Wyoming. In spite of the rambling characteristics of this peregrina-
tion, the leaders were entering the unknown with care and

skill and they carried with them the science of the times, as shown by an entry in Escalante's diary for that day:

Sept. 13, 1776. We took observations by the polar star and found ourselves in 40° 19′ latitude. Before Mid-day, we used the quadrant to confirm our observations by the sun and found ourselves in 40° 59′ 24″. Judging that the discrepancy might be caused by some variation in the needle, in order to find out, we secured the quadrant to observe the north star, which remains on the meridian of the compass at night. So soon as the north star was visible, the quadrant being on the meridian, we observed that the needle turned to the northeast. We again made the observation of the latitude by the north star and found the same, 40° 19′ as on the preceding night.

Any expedition capable of checking its latitude by a matter of minutes and seconds would have a pretty good idea of its whereabouts at all times, regardless of the terrain. Surely the "successful" expeditions of Alarcón and Diaz and Coronado in the sixteenth century could not have been more accurate. In fact, we know they were less.

On the twenty-fifth of September the party rested for a few days beside a lake at what is now the site of the city of Provo. This is Utah Lake but Escalante called it by another name.

We ascended a low hill and beheld the lake and extended valley of Nuestra Senora de la Merced de los Timpanogotzis, as we called it . . . large plains of good land for planting . . . and plenty, if irrigated, for two or even three large villages. This lake of the Timpanogotzis abounds in many kinds of good fish, and in geese and in other water fowl that we had not time to see. The Indians subsist on the abundant fish of the lake, for which reason the Yutas [Utes] call them fish-eaters.

The Indians called Yutas by Escalante were found by him to be "gentle and affable." They accepted his gifts and he took it for granted that they accepted his faith and his teachings, although the truth is that the priest could have made but little impression on the sluggish and phlegmatic Utes. Had he told them that he was an emissary of Jupiter or Buddha it would not have made any difference to the unimaginative Ute buck or squaw. But the Indians did tell the party of a great body of salt water to the north. Oddly, this phenomenon did not interest de Miera, and the expedition never saw the Great Salt Lake. They promised the Yutas that they would return and establish a Spanish colony and a Catholic mission, which caused no particular interest, and then moved on south and west, searching for the best route to California and Monterey. And from here on the going was rough.

The royal road to California was not to be found. To the west lay deserts and more deserts. One of the more forbidding they called El Desierto de Silvestre Velez de Escalante, a dubious honor perhaps, but this alkali waste of southwestern Utah is still known today as the Escalante Desert.

Things were rapidly pointing toward a crisis. The trip was not running according to schedule, the hardships became acute, and for the first time there was dissension within the party. On the sixteenth of October they reached their most westerly position, a point on what was to be in later years the Utah-Arizona boundary due south of the present Mormon town of St. George. Snow was falling in the high country which they had left behind, and the burning challenge of the Nevada deserts presented an unpleasant welcome to the west. California was months ahead, if ever they could make it at all. Winter was making a retracing of their route impossible. Their supplies were almost exhausted and so were their animals. The party was weary and undernourished and their clothes were ragged. They were almost three months re-moved from their original base of supplies in Santa Fe, and apparently the nearest source of relief was still Santa Fe.

What to do?

A council was called and seven opinions were expressed; the two Muniz brothers and Simon Luzero, the servant of Joaquin Lain, had no vote. The organization of the party was not on a democratic basis, and the capitalists and the priests jockeyed for leadership. The vote on whether to try to reach California at all odds, or to forego that objective and try to find some way to return to Santa Fe, was divided four to three, and this was so close as to demand a recount.

Don Bernardo de Miera was chagrined at the failure of the mission to find much more than a forbidding wilderness. He was the titular head and his authority carried weight. He voted most emphatically to go on. He would *not* return to Santa Fe empty-handed and dishonored.

Don Joaquin Lain was with him to the bitter end. Both had invested money in this expedition, and both would see it through.

With them, though not so emphatic, was Lorenzo de Oli-vares of El Paso. He still believed in the ultimate value of the expedition, but he was ill and weary. Perhaps it would be best to return to Santa Fe and try it again in the following year. Still, they were all partners in this venture, and if the leader was for going on, he would abide by that decision. Thus, after deliberation, he voted to go on to California.

Juan Pedro Cisneros of Zuni, and Juan de Aguilar of Bernalillo were of a different mind. California was not just over the next mountain range or beyond the next desert. It might be as much as another thousand miles across terrible country. They preferred to return home to Santa Fe and live to see California another day.

There remained Escalante and Dominguez, and Dominguez, be it remembered, was theoretically second in command. The two priests, very sensibly, voted to return to Santa Fe. Supplies were gone, and tempers were at the breaking point. Only more suffering in a hostile country lay ahead; but by working due east as directly as the topography would allow, they had a chance, no matter how slight, of reaching the Indian villages of the Painted Desert, and then Zuni and Santa Fe. When the poll was closed, the vote stood three for California and four for Santa Fe.

The California contingent was not satisfied, and a rift and separation seemed imminent. Escalante suggested to let the decision rest with God. There was no gainsaying this attitude and everyone agreed. Lots would be drawn: a long stick, California; a short stick, Santa Fe. Dominguez provided the prayers and Escalante provided the sticks and Don Bernardo de Miera had the honor of choosing. He hesitated, looked first east and then west, closed his eyes—and drew the short stick.

It was Santa Fe.

And here the leadership passed, if not politically, at least practically, from the aristocracy back to the church. Escalante and Dominguez took over, and in his journal, Escalante states, with a smile between the lines: "We all accepted this, thanks be to God, willingly and joyfully." Dominguez disposed of the sticks that Escalante had selected to indicate the decision of God. The blessed short stick meant Santa Fe. But when Dominguez destroyed them, he forgot to tell the others in the party that although the winning stick was definitely short, the other stick was even shorter.

But they were not yet out of the woods—or the deserts or the badlands. Carefully taking their bearings, the two priests set out for Santa Fe and the rest of the party followed. Again the expedition was a cohesive unit and of one mind. And while leadership had changed, spirits were higher. And

well they might be. For if Escalante and God had not contrived to convince the overly ambitious that a return to Santa
Fe was the only and wise decision, they would most surely
have died of thirst in the blistering deserts of Nevada.

As it was, they suffered mightily and were forced to eat
some of their pack animals, but all knew that they were now
moving under God's guidance and that somehow they would
get through. Such faith cannot fail. They got through.

Southward into Arizona the priests led the way, following
a valley one day to be known as Toroweap. Ahead lay the
great impassable gorge of the Grand Canyon, but they did
not know it. Within ten miles of this hopeless barrier, faith
led the way, and the priests turned east, missed the North
Rim of the canyon, and finally found Kanab Creek. From
here they needle-threaded along what in later years was to be
the Arizona-Utah border. It is safe to say that they never knew
how close to the Grand Canyon they were. But they must
have known of it, they must have sensed its proximity, and
carefully they avoided it.

East across the Kaibab Plateau they led the weary through
a country no white man had ever seen and yet, as true as the
terrain would allow, drawn like a steel filing to a magnet,
they marched straight to the only chance in a thousand they
had for survival.

For now it was no joke, and no game to be played with
sticks. It was life or death and every day counted, possibly
every hour. Neither Escalante nor Dominguez could have
known that the terrible Colorado River had an Achilles heel.
Neither priest could possibly have guessed or reasoned that
there was but one spot in the hundreds of miles either upstream or downstream that would permit them to cross. Yet
they marched straight to that spot.

Having avoided the yawning trap of the Grand Canyon,
they skirted Marble Canyon, picked their way high above

a violent and savage stream, and descended at last to the Colorado River by a side canyon so tortuous that the party had to hew its way by cutting steps down the side of a precipitous cliff in order to lead their animals down step by step. It was mountain climbing of the most dangerous order. But to the priests it was faith. They never doubted, and they were saved.

They reached the river on November 7, 1776, and this was the last little joker. For if the river is high at this point, a crossing is out of all reason; if it is low, a ford is possible though always dangerous. High water meant slow death by starvation; low water meant a chance to cross and reach the Hopi Indian villages a hundred and fifty miles to the south in Arizona's Painted Desert.

The priests were not worried. The water would have to be low, and it was.

And there, deep in a canyon of the mighty Colorado, they made, on the seventh day of November, 1776, the epic Crossing of the Fathers.

A certified copy of Escalante's diary containing a facsimile of the page describing the crossing was made by Charles F. Lummis from the original manuscript in the Ramirez collection, and may be seen in the library of the Southwest Museum in Los Angeles. It is a pity that such a fine scholar of the Southwest as Charles Lummis did not append his own translation. Interpreting freely but keeping as close to Escalante's style as practical, I offer the priest's own description as follows:

. . . here the river is very wide, and judging by the course it runs not very deep; but only by means of an adjacent canyon would we be able to descend to it. We sent two of our party to examine this [canyon] as well as the ford of the river, and they came back saying it would be too difficult. We did not give much credence to this information and we ourselves, accompanied by Don Juan

Pedro Cisneros, are determined to examine it tomorrow. Before dark the Janizaries arrived.

Seventh Day. We went very early to inspect the canyon and the ford, taking the two Janizaries [the Muniz brothers] as they might be able to cross the river since they were good swimmers. In descending the said canyon it was necessary for the protection of the animals, to make steps with an axe in a large rock for the distance of three rods or a little less. By this means the horses were able to pass, although without goods or packs. We went down the canyon, walked one mile, and arrived at the river; and we continued along the narrow strip of shore beside the water to its very limit which brought us to the widest part of the stream. And here, it appeared, was a ford.

The river is a hundred and fifty yards wide at this spot and the ford today is not straight and obvious, but follows treacherous sandbars. It could have been no better in 1776. Escalante's diary continues:

One of the Janizaries entered on foot and found it to be sufficiently good so that it was not necessary for him to swim. Following him on horseback we went in a little deeper, and in the middle of the river our two horses lost their footing and swam in the main channel which lay ahead. We held ourselves back, notwithstanding some danger, until the foot crosser returned from the far bank to conduct us. Thus we crossed with ease without straining the horses who arrived still swimming.

We informed our companions who had remained behind that with ropes and lariats they could make a cautious descent, bringing the harness, saddles, and other utensils by way of the large rock which was hazardous but not insuperable, hence to the head of the ford and by this means, they could bring the rest of the caravan down by the route which we had come. They did so, and by five in the afternoon they completed the crossing of the river. We gave praise to God, our Father, and fired some guns in token of the great relief we all felt in having conquered so great a barrier which had caused us so much work and delay.

Here is the literal description of the first crossing of the Colorado River in its canyon regions by white men. It is one more masterpiece of understatement. The chances for success were one in a thousand—a miracle. Elation must have been internal and external—quiet and vociferous. But Escalante, never an expansive man, is content to say "we fired some guns" when an imaginative emotionalist would have wept and shouted for joy.

Once on the south bank of the river the party was reasonably safe.

The last lap into Oraibi was painful and difficult, but the dangers were over. Faith—with a couple of short sticks—had won.

The threadbare and starving group reached Oraibi on November 16 and here they rested and recuperated. And at last, by way of Zuni, they returned over familiar ground to Santa Fe and marched into the surprised city on New Year's Day, 1777.

The exploit of Escalante and Dominguez is remarkable no matter how one looks at it. Whether it be their faith and trust in the efficacy of prayer, or whether the fabulous Bright Angel of the Grand Canyon region guided their footsteps to the only possible escape back to civilization, or whether it should be defined by the indefinable and called "a miracle"—no matter how we look at it, the whole story is amazing and incredible. But it happened.

De Miera and Company got nothing for their pains. The land over which they had struggled, rich in every mineral known to man, was discounted as worthless, its arable acreage negligible in view of the whole, and its aborigines backward and hardly worth converting and certainly not worth exploiting as workers or slaves. De Miera drew a large and detailed map of the region in Santa Fe in 1777. Nobody cared to study it. The Spanish Empire, long past its prime, was fast crumbling. The map was sent to Mexico City and finally to Spain. It is still gathering dust in the archives of the War Department in Madrid today. But Herbert S. Auerbach has published an excellent reproduction of it along with some pertinent comment in the *Utah Historical Quarterly*.

Escalante and Dominguez never returned to bring the faith to their Yuta Indians. The promised mission was never built; the fertile valleys of central Utah were forgotten; the sphere of Spanish influence moved no farther north than the headwaters of the Rio Grande. The de Miera expedition, penetrating almost to Wyoming, was the high-water mark of New Spain, and from there the Spanish tide receded.

The ineffective results of de Miera and Company had only a negative place in history. De Miera had not been backed by Mexico or Madrid. His was not a military expedition to forward the course of empire. He was merely a business man who had invested unwisely, and destiny never intended him to be another Cortes. His fiasco wrote finis to the flood tide of Spanish infiltration into the American West.

There were a couple of final laps, of course, notably a little-known expedition by Manuel Mestas in 1805 and an even more obscure party led by Mauricio Arze in 1813 into Utah. But these were quickly forgotten, and the great Rocky Mountain region and Great Basin area were practically virgin territory to the first American explorers, scouts, and trappers—the Patties, Jedediah Smith, and William Ashley, advance guards of the expanding United States in the eighteen twenties.

New Spain ceased to exist in 1821, and Mexico rose from its ashes. The new country had no more interest in Utah in 1821 than we have today in Betelgeuse—perhaps less. By

1846 the Mexican War was fought between Washington and Mexico City over who was going to get what in the American Southwest. As Mexico says today, "We compromised; the United States got it all." This is not entirely accurate. By the end of the war, 1848, Mexico had little more than a paper claim to the lands of Colorado, Utah, and Nevada, and this was due entirely to the failure to follow up the de Miera expedition. It was there for the taking in 1776, and New Spain didn't want it. Had she established garrisons and outposts along the de Miera route, it is entirely conceivable that the history of the American West would have followed quite a different pattern.

Today the de Miera expedition has become backstage history. Its leader is unknown, as Escalante and Dominguez have risen to the surface of the story for the few people who know of it at all. And about all that is popularly known about the two priests is that they crossed a river at some place, still inaccessible, called the Crossing of the Fathers. Who or what or where or why is of little concern. But *how* they ever found the crossing is truly a mystery. It was in the cards for Escalante and Dominguez and the rest of the party to perish in the rocky fastness of the Grand Canyon or any of the adjacent gorges. Only Escalante and the Bright Angel know why they did not.

Lieutenant Ives Is Not Amused

"AT LAST we reached the place where the river emerges from these horrid mountains," wrote James Ohio Pattie, "which so cage it up as to deprive all human beings of the ability to descend to its banks and make use of its waters. No mortal has the power of describing the pleasure I felt when I could once more reach the banks of the river."

James Ohio, and his father, Sylvester Pattie, were trappers who explored much of New Mexico and Arizona in 1825. They reached the lower Colorado in the vicinity of what is today Yuma and worked upstream, following the general course of the river, all the way through Utah and into Wyoming. Most of the time they didn't know where they were except "out west." They were the first white men to travel throughout the entire Rocky Mountain region and this achievement has been forgotten in the rising tide of history. Their exploit was remarkable, and an account of it was published in book form by John H. Wood, as edited by Timothy Flint, in Cincinnati in 1831. Yet the student of the American West will search a long time before he will find a copy of *The Personal Narrative of James O. Pattie of Kentucky* in American libraries.

The Patties skirted the Grand Canyon for its entire length and James Ohio later wrote in his book, "We were compelled to climb a mountain and travel along its acclivity, the river still in sight, and at an immense depth beneath us." For weeks they traveled overland, suffering at times for lack of food but surviving on whatever game they could kill. "It is this very long and formidable range of mountains," wrote James Ohio, "which has caused that this country has not been more explored."

Remarkable conclusion. He might as well have written: "The reason men have not explored the moon is due to the fact that they have not yet been able to reach it." But if Pattie's book is naive and humorless, it is important Americana. And significant is his dominating adjective—"horrid." It seems odd to us today that anyone summing up the Grand Canyon region would choose "horrid" as the quintessential description, yet the sober and literal Mr. Pattie is not inaccurate. The word derives from the Latin, meaning "rough," and rough the region was and is.

But one thing is certain: the Patties did not like it and said so. In this they were not alone.

The Patties left the only record of the country between the Spanish priests in 1776 and Lieutenant Joseph C. Ives in 1858, and like the Patties, Lieutenant Ives was not amused.

Jedediah Smith, a great name in the West, passed close to the Grand Canyon area in 1826, traveling southwest through Utah and descending the Virgin River to its confluence with the Colorado. He called the Colorado by still another name, the Seedskeedee. This is a Crow Indian word meaning Prairie Hen, apparently an inapt name until one realizes that the Crows lived far to the North in Wyoming where the headwaters of the Colorado's tributaries did indeed support range for prairie hens. Here it was the Seedskeedee River, so as far as Jedediah Smith was concerned, it was still the Seedskeedee at a point now inundated by Lake Mead back of Boulder

Dam. Smith went on west, leaving the canyon country to await the coming of Lieutenant Ives.

An official expedition to explore the Colorado River from the delta to the head of navigation, wherever that might prove to be, was instigated in 1857 in Washington by the Office of Explorations and Surveys.

Lieutenant Ives, who had seen some of the lower Colorado the year before, was put in charge. He was going to do it properly. A stern-wheeler was built in Philadelphia and given a trial run on the Delaware River in the spring of 1857. It worked perfectly on the Delaware, so there was no reason why it would not work on the Colorado. This was Washington reasoning on the part of gentlemen in the Office of Explorations and Surveys who had never been west of Harper's Ferry on the Potomac. The proud stern-wheeler, in honor of the office, was called the *Explorer* until the Colorado took it in hand.

The *Explorer* was dismantled and shipped in sections from Philadelphia by way of Panama to Robinson's Landing at the mouth of the Colorado. Here it was reassembled and trouble began. The strain on the vessel in the gentle Delaware proved to have been no test for the strain presented by the ten- and fifteen-foot waves at the tidal bore of the Colorado. No sooner was the *Explorer* launched than the Colorado gave it a playful slap and cracked the hull. For the first time, in what was to be a series of incidents, Lieutenant Ives was not amused.

This caused a delay until timbers and bolts could be sent from San Francisco, and the *Explorer* was patched up. But it never equaled its trial performance on the Delaware, nor was the Colorado yet through with it.

In spite of the elaborate preparations on the part of Washington, this expedition had not been well planned. There had been previous steamers on the Colorado—the *General Jessup* and the *Uncle Sam,* both of which had been ignominiously sent to the bottom by the river a few years earlier. Captain Johnson, who owned the *General Jessup,* tried again, and called his new boat the *Colorado,* in an effort to placate the river. It was a shallow draft stern-wheeler one hundred and twenty feet long and the river begrudgingly allowed it to operate for a number of years. Thus the *Colorado* had puffed and snorted up and down stream before the *Explorer* arrived. All Washington had needed to do was to charter the *Colorado* from Captain Johnson, whose boat was for rent, and thereby save the expense of designing, building, testing, dismantling, shipping, reassembling, and reconstructing the *Explorer*—all of which must have been extremely costly. But Washington didn't do things that way—in 1857.

Ives's ship was only half the length of Captain Johnson's *Colorado* which made her more maneuverable, but unfortunately Johnson was familiar with the river and Ives was not. Moreover, the human frailties were present and Ives and Johnson considered each other rivals. Probably Johnson resented not having a fat government contract for himself and his steamer, so just to show Washington what a mistake it had made he proceeded to steam to the head of navigation himself and what is more he did it before Ives could get there.

Lieutenant Ives, on a serious scientific expedition, chose to ignore Johnson's existence. After all, who was this river-runner to be recognized by the Office of Explorations and Surveys? Nobody.

It was December 30, 1857, before the *Explorer* could be repaired and made ready for action. The next day the great trip began, and in January, 1858, the party reached Yuma. Johnson was far ahead in his steamer and doing nicely, but the poor *Explorer* was having a bad time of it. She ran aground; even with full steam up, she was swept downstream by the changing current, and she was rocked and shipped an alarming amount of water. Everyone in the party agreed on one point; the *Explorer* was the ideal ship to explore the Delaware River. At times she had to be towed from the shore, and Ives was unable to enlist the towing service of the Cocopahs or the Yumans as Alarcón had done, for now these people knew that white men did not come from the sun after all. The Indians sat on the banks and laughed.

Somehow the party managed to move upstream and they passed the site of Needles. Here they were watched by Mojave Indians, and one of these was hired by Ives as a guide. The Lieutenant's choice was excellent. The Indian's name was Ireteba and Ives gives him full credit as an assistant, saying, "This Indian is the finest I have ever met . . . he is invaluable . . . quickly learns English words . . . and is expert at drawing maps on the ground." The *Explorer*, however, was still in trouble, and Ives is loyal to his ship and apologizes for it by saying: "It is probable that there is not one season in ten when the *Explorer* would encounter one fourth the difficulty that she had during the unprecedentedly low stage of water."

They passed Johnson who was now coming downstream, having reached the head of navigation in Black Canyon where Boulder Dam stands today. It is said that Ives failed to return Johnson's salute, though it is hard to believe this of the Lieutenant. In his account of his expedition, however, he barely mentions Johnson and never says a word about the rival steamer.

At low water there are small rapids even this far down on the river, and through these hazards the *Explorer* had to be towed. That she survived at all is a wonder. At last they came to Black Canyon. So little was known about this country in 1858 that Ives thought this might be the beginning of the Grand Canyon, though he quickly learned better. The battered *Explorer* puffed bravely on and all hands rejoiced as she seemed to take a new lease on life and gain speed. The current slackened and Ives counted on a good day's run. It was full speed ahead.

Then came a terrible crash.

The *Explorer* had run into a sunken rock, splitting her bow. So abrupt was her stop that men on the forward deck were thrown overboard, those on the afterdeck were thrown into the machinery, the boiler was set askew on its support, the entire wheelhouse was ripped off, the stern-wheel was jammed, the steampipe was broken, leaks occurred in her bottom, the funnel leaned like the tower of Pisa, and the whole ship groaned like a harpooned and dying whale.

The man who had been holding the sounding pole at the bow was fished out of the river. It had been his job to keep calling soundings, and as soon as he could talk, with water still running out of his mouth and ears he shouted, "Egad, Lieutenant, I believe we may have reached the head of navigation! Stop her!"

Egad, they had.

And, egad, the Colorado had stopped her for good. In her sinking condition the crew managed to get her onto a sandbank. And there she rested, done in.

Lieutenant Ives was not amused. He turned from the wreck of the *Explorer* and looked at the country. In his record he mentions reaching "the head of navigation" and he describes not the *Explorer's* condition, but the scenery instead. It was a much more pleasant subject. "No description," he wrote, "can convey an idea of the varied and majestic grandeur of this peerless waterway. Wherever the river makes a turn, the entire panorama changes, and one startling novelty after another appears and disappears with bewildering rapidity." What most men would have written under the circumstances wouldn't have been fit to print. And what is more, Ives well knew that Captain Johnson had steamed at least twenty miles farther upstream than his wreck of an *Explorer*. The Lieutenant showed great self-control indeed, and from his composition one might say his talents were misplaced; he could have written excellent travel-folder copy.

Steamboating was now out of the range of possibility. Ives was well supplied with an overland pack train. So he returned to the Mojave country at Needles and reorganized his expedition. From now on they would go overland, and here Ireteba proved his inestimable value.

The party moved northeast from Needles, following a route similar to that taken by Padre Garces in 1776.

Descending Diamond Creek in northwestern Arizona, they again reached the Colorado River and this time they were in the western reaches of the Grand Canyon. With Lieutenant Ives was Dr. J. S. Newberry, an eminent geologist of the times, and also two artists, F. W. Egloffstein and H. B. Mollhausen. These men were stunned and awed by the proportions of the Grand Canyon country and Ives describes Newberry as being in a geologist's heaven. Perhaps the two artists were in a kind of heaven, too, but their sketches of the locality —particularly Egloffstein's—are surprising. These drawings serve to illustrate Ives' *Report on the Colorado River of the West*, printed as a senatorial document in Washington in 1861. Egloffstein's work is anything but realistic. The magnificent proportions of the canyons are exaggerated in order to create an awesome effect, and as impressions they serve a purpose, but as reproductions of what Egloffstein saw they were about as faithful as illustrations of scenes from the *Divine Comedy*.

At the mouth of Diamond Creek and the Colorado River, much farther upstream than the poor *Explorer* could have reached except in pieces, Ives called the spot "Big" Canyon. The name Grand Canyon was not yet in use and it remained for Major John Wesley Powell to christen it thus in 1869.

The Ives expedition, led by Ireteba, continued east over

rough and rugged terrain. The going was difficult and the party endured the hardships, believing they were the first to traverse this area. They knew nothing of Father Garces or even the Patties. The farther east they went the less Ireteba knew of the country. They were now beyond the homeland of the Mojaves and into that of the Walapais, and Ireteba procured a couple of Walapai guides.

Lieutenant Ives was not favorably impressed with these latter Indians. "They stink," he frankly said, and commented later that they did not live up to the Fenimore Cooper tradition of what Indians should be. "They are a lowly type and to eat is their one idea." Nevertheless, it was a case of Walapai guides or no guides at all. And the trip was made even more unpleasant a few days later when Ireteba would go no farther. He shook hands with Ives, and the Lieutenant loaded him down with presents and he returned to his people at Needles. Twenty-four hours later both Walapai guides disappeared, leaving the party stranded in the high desert country of arroyos, canyons, and mesas.

At night, however, the Walapais returned, saying that they had merely gone to search for water. They led the party to a small spring and here they camped. In the morning the Walapais were gone again, and this time they took all the food and blankets that they could carry. As guides, Lieutenant Ives found them disappointing. He dismissed their peccadilloes with a few words and again described the scenery.

They were getting into high country, and the altitude and the cold increased as they went on. Not only were they having Indian trouble, but also water trouble and mule trouble. When they left a small spring it was a question of whether they would find water again that day or not—or for a number of days. There was no way to explain this to the mules. They weren't thirsty in the morning and they wouldn't drink. Ives wrote, "The mules, ignorant of what was before them, refused, as mules often do, to drink on the morning before leaving camp." Three dry days went by and Ives adds, "They became too thirsty to graze and filled the air with their distressing cries." It was all very unpleasant indeed.

They found more Walapais and by commandeering and bribing, they succeeded in retaining them for guides. Why this party, twenty-five strong, was in such dire need of guidance is not clear. Certainly one experience with the untrustworthy Walapais should have been sufficient. But this was a scientific expedition and as such it must have its native guide. Things were done that way. These new Walapais, of course, ran away at the first opportunity taking a mule with them.

The party had been equipped for the warm region of the Colorado River, and now they were at an elevation of more than five thousand feet and constantly getting higher. They lost a man who went out on his own to hunt deer and a day was wasted while the others searched for him. A snowstorm broke and the man barely got back ahead of it. What Ives said to the man is not recorded, but it is certain that neither of them was amused by the incident.

It was the twelfth of April, 1858, and the snow, fortunately, or unfortunately, did not last long. In fact, it melted within twenty-four hours and again there was the problem of water. This time the parched mules solved it in their own mulish way. They craftily waited their chances and then broke away and ran or trotted all the way back to the last spring. The men had to pursue them on foot, and if anyone has ever tried to overtake a mule who doesn't want to be caught, he can well understand the irritation of the Ives Expedition. The mules kept in sight but just out of reach and the party had to follow them back almost to the point where they had parted with their Mojave guide, Ireteba. By this time, nobody, not even the geologists or the artists, was amused.

It might have seemed like common sense at this time to go the mules one better and return all the way to Needles. But Ives, quite understandably, could not bring himself to do this. His river trip had been a fiasco; another steamer had reached the head of navigation instead of his *Explorer;* and the whole mission to explore the Colorado River had become demoralized in high and dry and cold mountains. This was no report to make to Washington. So the mules were watered and they began again.

Back over the Garces trail they went and this time they penetrated farther into the wilderness of mesas, canyons, and badlands that buttress the Grand Canyon country on the west. A dizzy trail wound around a cliff and the party moved in single file. Without knowing it they were following in Garces' very footsteps, for this was the Walapai Trail which led then and leads today to the long hidden canyon of the Havasupai Indians deep in a side cleft of the Grand Canyon.

"I rode first," wrote Ives in his report, "and the rest of the party and train followed one by one—looking very much like a row of insects crawling upon the side of a building."

After a mile of this the trail narrowed so that there were only three inches between the mule and a thousand-foot drop.

"The sight made my head swim," continues Ives, "and I dismounted and got ahead of the mule, a difficult and delicate operation, which I was thankful to have safely performed. A part of the men became so giddy that they were obliged to creep on their hands and knees, being unable to walk or stand."

At last they reached a place so dangerous that the mules would go no farther. Fortunately there was a wide spot nearby where the animals could be turned around. The mules were then sent back with some of the party to form a base camp, and Ives and the others determined to continue on foot.

The Lieutenant's first hand account is vivid and colorful and should be told in his own words.

Lieutenant Tipton, Mr. Egloffstein, Mr. Peacock and myself, with a dozen men, formed the party to explore the canyon. It was about five miles to the precipice. [The point of farthest advance of the mules.] The descent of the latter was accomplished without serious trouble. In one or two places the path traversed smooth inclined ledges, where the insecure footing made the crossing dangerous. The bottom of the canyon, which from the summit looked smooth, was covered with hills thirty or forty feet high. Along the center we were surprised to find an inner canyon, a kind of under-cellar, with low walls at the starting point, which were soon converted into lofty precipices, as the base of the ravine sank deeper and deeper into the earth. Along the bottom of this gorge we followed the trail, distinctly seen when the surface was not covered with rocks. Every few moments, low falls and ledges, which we had to jump or slide down, were met with, till there had accumulated a formidable number of obstacles to be encountered in returning.

This, be it remembered, is but a side canyon of the Grand Canyon proper, and Lieutenant Ives' description of the terrain in 1858 might just as well have been written to describe the area today. Man has touched this part of Arizona hardly at all. He continues:

Like other canyons, it was circuitous, and at each turn we were impatient to find something novel or interesting. We were deeper in the bowels of the earth than we had ever been before, and surrounded by walls and towers of such imposing dimensions that it would be useless to attempt describing them; but the effects of magnitude had begun to pall, and the walk from the foot of the precipice was monotonously dull; no sign of life could be discerned above or below. At the end of thirteen miles from the precipice an obstacle presented itself that there seemed to be no possibility of overcoming. A stone slab, reaching from one side of the canyon to the other, terminated the place which we were descending. Looking over the edge it appeared that the next level was forty feet below. This time there was no trail along the side bluffs, for these were smooth and perpendicular. A spring of water rose from the bed of the canyon above, and trickled over the ledge forming a pretty cascade. It was supposed that the Indians must have come to this point merely to procure water, but this theory was not altogether satisfactory, and we sat down upon the rocks to discuss the matter.

Mr. Egloffstein lay down by the side of the creek, and projecting his head over the ledge to watch the cascade, discovered a solution of the mystery. Below the shelving rock, and hidden by it and the fall, stood a crazy looking ladder made of rough sticks bound together with thongs of bark.

This was "the ladder of wood," described by Padre Garces, which forced him to leave his mule and continue on foot. For the first time in eighty-two years the white race had come again, and the solitary priest was at last followed by the soldier, the scientist, and the artist. Probably it was the same ladder with only minor repairs that Garces had used, but this party did not have the priest's blind faith or good luck. Ives continues with this description of the ladder:

It was almost perpendicular, and rested upon a bed of angular stones. The rounds had become rotten from the incessant flow of water. Mr. Egloffstein, anxious to have the first view of what was below, scrambled over the ledge and got his feet on the upper round. Being of solid weight, he was too much for the insecure fabric, which commenced giving way. One side, fortunately stood firm, and holding on to this with a tight grip, he made a precipitate descent. The other side and all the rounds broke loose and accompanied him to the bottom in a general crash, effectually cutting off the communication.

Leaving us to devise means of getting him back he ran to the bend to explore. The bottom of the canyon had been reached. He found that he was at the edge of a stream, ten or fifteen yards wide, fringed with cottonwoods and willows. [Havasu Creek as it is today.] The walls of the canyon spread out for a short distance leaving room for a narrow belt of bottom land, on which were fields of corn and a few scattered huts.

This is the heart of Havasupailand and the tiny and remote settlement of Supai, Arizona, the most inaccessible post office in the United States even now. There are two or three Indians living there today who were little boys at the time of Egloffstein's inglorious arrival bottom first. And the venerable chief Watahomogie, if he is well over a hundred as his reputation insists, must have been a young man in his prime in 1858. Lieutenant Ives did not descend the last long step into Cataract Canyon and the home of the smiling people. The impetuous Mr. Egloffstein had precluded that. But Ives could scramble up to a vantage point and look below.

A place was found near the ledge where one could clamber a little way up the wall, and we thus got a view of the valley. The canyon, Mr. Egloffstein saw, could not be followed far; there were cascades just below. He perceived, however, that he was very near to its mouth, though perhaps at a thousand feet greater altitude, and an Indian pointed out the exact spot where it united with the canyon of the Rio Colorado.

Egloffstein was not as near to the Colorado as he thought. It is a good six miles from the heart of Havasupailand to the Colorado over a tough trail and there are three more large waterfalls in between. Ives continues his observations:

[87]

These Yampais [his name for Havasupais] did not differ much from the Walapais in general appearance. They were perhaps a trifle cleaner and more respectable. It is probable that, all told, they do not number more than two hundred persons. One of them accompanied Mr. Egloffstein to the foot of the ledge, and intimated a willingness to go with us to camp, but when he saw the broken ladder he gave up his intention. The accident did not appear otherwise to concern him. There must have been some other trail leading to the retreat, for the use of the ladder had evidently been long abandoned.

There was, of course, the Topocoba Trail by means of which Padre Garces left. This is the main trail today for supplies and occasional tourists from Grand Canyon to Supai. In 1858 it must have been just as hazardous as the ground over which Ives had come, but he never saw it. If he was a little provoked with the artist for preventing him from being the first of the party to descend to the floor of the canyon, he conceals his opinion and continues his narrative:

Having looked at all that was to be seen, it now remained to get Mr. Egloffstein back. The slings upon the soldiers' muskets were taken off and knotted together, and a line thus made which reached to the bottom. Whether it would support his weight was a matter of experiment. The general impression was that it would not, but of the two evils—breaking his neck or remaining among the Yampais—he preferred the former, and fastened the strap around his shoulder. It was a hard straight lift. The ladder pole was left and rendered great assistance both to us and the rope, and the ascent was safely accomplished. We invited the Indian to follow Mr. Egloffstein's example, but this he energetically declined. The examination being finished it was time to return.

It is clear from the account that F. M. Egloffstein was the only member of the expedition to set foot in Cataract Canyon and mingle with the Havasupais. And he was there for a matter of hours only. This explains why the Ives report lacks the detail about the Havasupai people which is present in the diary of Padre Garces who spent five days among them.

The party returned to its base camp and continued to explore the area and reached a point on the rim of what Ives still called "Big" Canyon. This was a considerable distance west of the present El Tovar Hotel and Bright Angel Trail, and the party was greatly impressed. Ives says, "We paused in wondering delight. There are fissures so profound the eye cannot penetrate their depths . . . and slender spires that seem tottering on their bases shoot up thousands of feet from the vaults below."

This was literary enthusiasm of the moment. Ives' sense of appreciation was always great and his report is consistently well written. It was only that the difficulties and disappointments and hardships of the trip as a whole dampened his ardor. Throughout his writing there is an unselfish heroism and a zealous desire to perform his job faithfully. And there is a constant attempt to play down the vicissitudes and play up the scenery whenever the going was rough.

After having examined the area thoroughly, however, his scenic escapism collapses with a bang and the long-delayed honest reaction comes forth. The whole expedition had failed to come off with the glory that he had expected. It had been plain hard and thankless work. And both the river and the terrain were more than he had been prepared to combat. After moving south and east from the Grand Canyon to the area around the San Francisco Peaks, the party worked its way east, through the Painted Desert and the Hopi country and concluded their travels at the government post of Fort Defiance in eastern Arizona. Ives was glad that it was over, and he never expected to do it again. Oddly enough he never learned that Cardenas had been there in 1540, and Garces in 1776, and that Escalante and Dominguez had crossed the Colorado in its canyon regions the same year as Garces. Nor had he ever heard of the two Patties, father and son, who skirted the Grand Canyon in 1825.

At his "Camp 74" on April 18, 1858, he wrote what he really thought, and such a truly honest statement should be quoted to show not so much what Ives thought of the area as to show what the area had done to Ives.

The region is altogether valueless. It can be approached only from the south, and after entering it there is nothing to do but leave. Ours has been the first, and doubtless will be the last, party of whites to visit this profitless locality. It seems intended by nature that the Colorado River along the greater part of its lonely and majestic way, shall be forever unvisited and undisturbed. The handful of Indians that inhabit the sequestered retreats where we discovered them, have probably remained in the same condition, and of the same number, for centuries. The country could not support a large population, and by some provision of nature they have ceased to multiply. . . .

In other words, it is neither pleasant nor profitable; nobody will ever go there again, and the river and the canyon are best forgotten once and for all.

Lieutenant Ives took his report to Washington and remained on the Atlantic seaboard. When the Civil War broke out in 1861, Ives joined the Confederacy. He fought bravely and well and gave his life for the cause of the South. He was an earnest and likable man and he deserved a happier fame.

Today the terrible river has long since eradicated all traces of his ineffective *Explorer* and the country over which he passed left no trace of his journey. The Grand Canyon swallowed him up, like all the others, and if it were not for the

Senate report he would be completely forgotten. In fact, another party, moving through the raw country ten years later, naïvely declared; "We are the first white men to explore this part of North America and probably none will follow us. . . ."

And the Grand Canyon merely yawned.

Life at Lee's Ferry

Sparse terrain, he would be completely forgotten. In fact, in most parts, moving through the one country on some day's much distant... ... ... despite the part... ... ... how trees And the Grand Canyon merely a sketch

Towns, or communities, or settlements of any kind in the Grand Canyon region have been rare. The nature of the country precludes any permanent civilizing force. There is Grand Canyon village, of course, on the South Rim which owes its existence to the National Park Service and the tourist business. There is the Indian village of Supai deep in Cataract Canyon, and there is the Union Pacific's lodge on the North Rim. The only other settlements along the great gorge between Green River, Utah, and Boulder Dam (if you skip Phantom Ranch on Bright Angel Creek) are Hite and Lee's Ferry.

Hite, Utah, near the mouth of the Dirty Devil River, usually has a population of one and never more than three. It is merely a ranch and a base of supplies for mining operations and to get to it is an expedition in itself even today.

Lee's Ferry is about thirty-five miles downstream from the Crossing of the Fathers and about six miles upstream from Marble Canyon where the Navajo Bridge carries the modern highway across the river forty stories above high-water mark. The opening of the bridge in 1929 put the ferry out of business. The motoring public no longer has any reason for going to the old ferry site and therefore few tourists ever see one of the West's historical landmarks. In a sense that is too bad, although a visit to Lee's Ferry today requires an active im-

[92]

agination in order to reconstruct some of the scenes that have been played there.

The Colorado River is wide at this spot, and it is joined by a tributary from the north, the Paria—pronounced Pah-reé-a—supposedly a Ute word meaning "elk water." It is never possible to ford the river at this point, but the water is smooth enough so that a flatboat or a scow can be navigated back and forth.

Two well-known names in Southwestern history are associated with the spot. One was famous and he was Jacob Hamblin, scout, frontiersman, and general advance man for Brigham Young and the Mormons of Utah. The other was infamous, and he was John Doyle Lee, whose name is marred by the Mountain Meadows Massacre in which some rabid and overzealous Mormons (Lee was one of them) killed a hundred and twenty men, women, and children, simply because they were not Mormons.

Brigham Young was interested in expanding the empire of the Latter Day Saints southward, even though that empire was effectually shut in on the southeast and south by the Colorado River, and he sent Jacob Hamblin as a kind of minister without portfolio into Arizona Territory to see how the land looked for settlement. This was in 1858. Hamblin, with the help of Ute Indians, found the ford where Escalante and Dominguez crossed the Colorado in 1776 and he is presumed to be the first white man to follow the two priests. He traveled extensively throughout the region and as he was a simple, honest, quiet-speaking man who always kept his word, he became known to all Indians as a friend. Navajos, Utes, Paiutes, Walapais, Hopis, and Havasupais—all knew Jacob Hamblin and all accounted him something of a white medicine man. When he said he would be at a certain place, he was always there. If he wanted to meet an Indian thirty days later he would give him a sack with thirty cedar berries in it, and tell the Indian to throw away one berry with each sun. When the last berry was gone Jacob would be back. And to the Indian's wonder he always was.

After he became familiar with the Grand Canyon country, Hamblin noted the smooth water at the meeting of the Paria with the Colorado—and he managed to effect a crossing at that spot by means of a log raft. Since Hamblin reported all of his findings to Salt Lake City, Brigham Young realized that the only avenue of trade into Arizona that was not blocked by the canyon country must be at this crossing. The ford of Escalante and Dominguez was far too dangerous and difficult to be practical.

The Mountain Meadows case made it necessary for the ring-leaders to "make themselves scarce" and Young is supposed to have told John Doyle Lee to take his wives and his bags and his luggage and move out of Utah. An ideal place would be the Colorado at the Paria where Lee could have the ferry right on what was going to be the only Mormon road into central Arizona. Here he would be reasonably safe from any United States marshals who might search high and low over Utah and never find him, for he would be over the line in Arizona. Brigham Young was "the Lion of the Lord," and when the Lion roared the common folk obeyed, for the Lion's voice was one with God. Lee moved to the Colorado River.

It was now 1872.

Lee was sixty years old; he didn't take all of his wives, but left the older women in Utah. How many wives accompanied him to the Colorado is not known but probably half a dozen, and Mrs. Lee, the seventeenth (Rachel), and Mrs. Lee, the eighteenth (Emma) were there when the second river expedition of Major Powell reached the scene the same year.

It should be stated that while John Doyle Lee was guilty of murder, he was not the arch-criminal that tradition has created. He was the pawn of the three Saints who plotted the cold-blooded slaying of the one hundred and twenty Gentile emigrants at Mountain Meadows, and it was Lee who finally paid with his life for the crimes of men even more fanatic than he. From the day of the mass murder in 1857 he never had a moment of peace. He moved about Utah in an effort to keep ahead of government investigators, and there is one persistent story that he spent a few years in hiding with the Havasupai Indians in Cataract Canyon, and that he brought them their peach and apricot seedlings and taught them improved methods of farming. There is no substantiation for this story and it is probably untrue. The Havasupais got their peach and apricot sprays from the Hopis with whom they have traded for many generations, and thus the people of the sky-blue water never saw the unhappy Mormon.

So in 1872 Lee's Ferry was founded. At first it was a town of Lees only, as a man who had eighteen wives also had a brood of children in numerical proportion. Jacob Hamblin was on the scene from time to time and in 1873 he laid out a wagon road south from Lee's Ferry to Tuba City, a Mormon mission and trading post in the Navajo country.

A town founded by a murderer practicing polygamy on the world's most dangerous river has a distinction that few communities can boast. But a recognized town it was, for Lee's Ferry became a post office. There were eight buildings in two rows of four each with a street between them. They were all made of rocks and plastered with adobe mud. One was the main house and the others were storehouses and homes of various wives. High on a hill overlooking the Paria and the Colorado and the surrounding country, Lee built a lookout so that he, or one of his family, could spot any strangers long before they arrived. One of the buildings in the "town" was also a kind of fort. It had very small windows and holes from which rifles could be fired. Lee said it was to be used in case of an Indian attack, but more than likely he intended it as a last-ditch stand if and when federal officers should arrive and try to arrest him. In the rich adjacent bottom land of the Paria, there were fields of vegetables, alfalfa, fruit trees, and grazing land for livestock.

Lee called the place Lonely Dell and indeed it was that. His ferry business he called Saint's Ferry, and a desire to keep his own name out of circulation is evident. Neither name stuck, however, and both the place and its reason for being were forever made known in the name Lee's Ferry.

When a weary traveler arrived he always found that Lee was not at home. If he came into town from Utah he would note a scurrying of women and children into buildings where they would peer out at him. And if he looked at the building used as a fort, he would find the seventeenth Mrs. Lee training a shotgun on him until his identity could be established as friendly. Rachel Lee, moreover, was said to be a crack shot. After this unusual reception, and after the stranger had declared that he wished only to be ferried across the Colorado, Lee would appear from one of the houses or come striding down from the lookout. Then the stranger, even if he were a Gentile, would be made welcome, probably fed, and ferried across and sent on his way.

If the stranger came up from central Arizona, he would have to "hallo" across the river until Rachel came over with the ferry and the shotgun to ask his qualifications. If Rachel was a sergeant-at-arms, Emma (thirty-five years younger than Lee and his last bride) was a chef supreme. All visitors, from the second Powell expedition on until 1877 when Lee left his lonely dell for the last time, declared that the food was good at Lee's Ferry—new vegetables, freshly killed meat, game in and out of season, raw milk, and fresh butter. There were plenty of wives to keep a good household. Life at Lee's Ferry may have been unusual, but life there was undeviatingly Mormon.

If the traveler rested overnight, Lee would entertain his guest with prayer and tell his version of the Mountain Meadows Massacre and emphasize his innocence. It was a wishful tale; Lee never told the truth until he broke down after his eventual arrest and wrote, of his own volition, a full confession of his part in the crime. Ironically enough, he was never sought at Lee's Ferry and all his precautions were unnecessary. But after a few years he made a furtive trip to the town of Panguitch, Utah, where another wife maintained a residence. A United States marshal had got wind of this visit and he caught Lee hiding and trembling in a pigpen. Two years later, after two trials, Lee was executed by a firing squad on the exact spot where his perfidy had helped to disarm and betray the one hundred and twenty victims of Mormon hate and religious unbalance. In a sense he paid the penalty for other Mormons, higher in the church than he, who were never brought to trial.

The first ferry was one of Major Powell's boats which had been battered by rapids and was no longer in good condition. Lee repaired it and it saw desultory service back and forth across the Colorado. It was not satisfactory, however, as it had never been designed for such a purpose.

Lee then brought timbers from the Kaibab Forest, sixty miles away. A flat-bottomed ferryboat was built, large enough to accommodate two wagons and teams. This awkward affair was piloted across by Lee and his sons, Charlie and Rains, and it seldom made the trip without at least a minor calamity of some sort, or perhaps a major tragedy. The trick was to use the downstream current to get it across and the downstream current to get it back. This left it well below the starting point so it had to be towed back upstream for its next trip. One story, which may be apocryphal, tells of the Lee's Ferry sheep racket. The pilots became so expert that they could cause the craft to tip by allowing the current to strike it at a certain angle. When it was packed with sheep the tip would throw half a dozen or more animals off and the helpless owner would see them being swept downstream. It was a loss to him, but not a serious loss, and there was no way to retrieve them. Once across, the shepherd went on his way, knowing that the ewes would soon produce more lambs and the number of sheep thus be restored. Sheep, however, can swim, and as there are no bad rapids at this point to dash them to pieces, they were able to get to shore only a mile or less downstream. By that time the shepherd had gone, so the Lees kept the sheep. At first they had only a few, but in time they had a flock. If the tale is true, it is no wonder the mutton was always good at the dinner table.

At times, however, there were unpremeditated accidents. When the ferry was heavily loaded it was in danger of getting out of control, and when the boat was tipped and the load shifted, it always got out of control. Animals and men were pitched into the river; supplies were lost; and on May 28, 1876, no less a person than Bishop Lorenzo W. Roundy of Salt Lake City, on his way to the mission among the Navajos, was thrown into the river and drowned in the swift current.

This kind of disaster was not uncommon up until 1929 when the ferry ceased operations and traffic moved by Navajo Bridge. As late as 1927 the ferryboat was whirled and dipped while it was carrying two Studebaker cars. Both automobiles were lost in the river. One of the ferrymen saw that one of the cars lay submerged in a spot that did not prevent salvage. A month after the accident when the owner had collected his insurance, the ferryman managed to haul the wreck out of the river. The body of the car was useless and so apparently was the engine. But this man took the engine apart, cleaned out the grit and the sand, soaked the parts in oil, reassembled it, poured in some gasoline, and it ran. Presumably it is still generating the power that is consumed locally. Thus Lee's

Ferry has its own way of taking its toll; sheep in the eighteen seventies, and a motor in the nineteen twenties.

After the execution of Lee, his eighteenth wife remained at the ferry and bravely tried to operate it alone. Her children were only seven and eight years old and the children of Lee's other wives were either grown up or approaching middle age. They were not interested in Lonely Dell and never returned to it. Only Emma Lee ran the ferry until 1879 when she sold it to the Mormon church for three thousand dollars.

The church held title to the ferry and leased it to the Johnson brothers, Price and Elmer. This family continued to live at the spot until 1935, when, for polygamous reasons, they moved to Short Creek which is also in Arizona just below the Utah line.

Polygamy was one of the tenets of Mormonism which Brigham Young steadfastly refused to renounce. It was not until thirteen years after Brigham's death—1890—that the church under the leadership of Wilford Woodruff legislated against polygamy. It was not a moral issue but a political issue. Utah could not become a state as long as polygamy was legal. Statehood was essential; economics was stronger than the Revelation as given to Joseph Smith and printed in *Doctrine and Covenants*. To have more than one wife became a crime, except to those who winked at it. At Lee's Ferry, miles from anywhere, they didn't even bother to wink at it. Let Utah become a state; they were in Arizona and Arizona was only a territory whose law never penetrated to this wild spot. The Johnson brothers went on marrying wife after wife.

Polygamy, as an accepted civic principle of life at Lee's Ferry, continued until 1935, and only stopped then because the prolific Johnsons moved to Short Creek where there were many sympathizers and diehards who had set up a "cohab" community. Cohab is merely slang for polygamist, indicating plural cohabitation.

[99]

In 1927 Arizona said the church in Salt Lake City should do something about the conditions at Lee's Ferry. The church said the crime was being practiced in Arizona, so Arizona should do something about it. So Arizona did: the state rented one building at Lee's Ferry for a school and sent a teacher to instruct the thirty-odd Johnson children who were growing up there in 1927. The church said that wouldn't put a stop to it; the state said the children, regardless of legality, were citizens of Arizona and Arizona was proud of her school system. An appeal was made to the Governor. He drove up from Phoenix and passed through Lee's Ferry and said, "Hell, if I had to live here I'd want more than one wife myself." And to his chauffeur, "Drive faster!"

In 1935 the church tried to crack down. In so doing it unearthed a lot of "cohab" sympathizers in Arizona's northern strip. The sunbaked town of Short Creek became the new Millennial City. Polygamous-minded Mormons of the old order came from far and wide. The church hesitated to act because it meant a lot of unsavory publicity. Arizona didn't mind because it was making the front pages of newspapers. Let Nevada have the divorce racket, Arizona was developing the crackpot marriage racket. When questioned, the advocates of the Revelation declared their adherence to polygamic theocracy in their own manner of expression, "You got to foller the laws of God er man; we's a-follerin' God, by God. It's writ in the book!" And they changed the name of Short Creek to the City of Fair Colors.

All this was during the relief period of the early nineteen thirties. It became a headache to the relief administrators to determine how to dole out money to a family declaring itself made up of one husband, five wives, and fourteen children. Especially when, with the relief money, the husband might take a new wife. Life at Lee's Ferry had indeed made a contribution to the West. It was something that the sensible

Mormon Church of 1935 wanted to forget but could not. And even for Arizona it began to get beyond the joke stage when the influx of "cohabs" at the City of Fair Colors began to swing the control of the electoral vote of the county. That was serious; both Mormon Church and State of Arizona joined hands in an effort to put an end to this social anachronism.

One unforeseen element came to the assistance of church and state. It had been revealed to the Prophet, Joseph Smith, back in 1830 when Mormonism was born, that if a woman were a virgin, and not promised in matrimony, any man might marry her regardless of the wife or wives he already had, provided he could support her. Relief money in 1935 made the support, such as it was, possible. The result was that the City of Fair Colors exhausted its supply of eligible virgins and the whole thing came to an end. Just to put the stamp of finality upon it, Arizona law sent two of the bitterest recalcitrants to the penitentiary.

The City of Fair Colors collapsed, and then the threatened boom of several thousand "cohabs" melted away. The name was changed back to Short Creek. And Lee's Ferry, which was responsible for the whole mess by keeping polygamy alive all through the years, became a guest ranch under new management.

The visitor today will find that the area looks much the same as it did when John Doyle Lee first settled there in 1872.

III

Row Your Boat

THE COLORADO RIVER AND ITS WATERSHED

The river, from Wyoming to its mouth, is more
than 2300 miles long — second only to the
Mississippi-Missouri in the United States.

Row Your Boat

THE Colorado is the most dangerous river in the world. And it is one of the longest and fastest in North America. Moreover, it is one of the most unpredictable. Even today only small portions of it are known and understood by the general public. The stream flows through canyons hundreds of miles long and hundreds of miles from a railroad, through country that is desolate and untouched by man, and almost all of which is either mountainous or desert. Except for the fact that the sea into which it finally pours is never sunless, it might well have been named Alph.

Before Boulder Dam was built there was not a single town on the Colorado between Green River, Utah, and Needles, California (excepting Lee's Ferry), a distance of more than eight hundred miles, and there were only two or three points along this course that it could even be crossed. It is a wild river surging through wild country, and in proportion to the number of men who have tried to make use of it, it has taken a high toll of lives.

Also, it is a river of many characteristics; in some spots it is placid, in others it is choked with rapids; at some places it is a hundred yards wide and at others it is four hundred, and at flood stage near the mouth it may be several miles across. At all times it is heavy with silt, and the government river-gauge station near the mouth of Bright Angel Creek has estimated that it carries a million tons of sediment past that point every twenty-four hours. When it is really furious it has hurled as much as twenty-seven million tons of pulverized rock and sand past the gauge in a single day. It travels at a rate of two miles an hour to twenty miles an hour, and even more. This, for a river, is express-train speed.

It has more than one personality, and to look at the reddish muddy water flowing quietly over sandbars at Yuma and to recall the roaring swirling rapids of Cataract Canyon which have smashed boats and men, is to understand that here is a schizophrenic. It is at once fascinating and dangerous, Jekyll and Hyde, and there is no river like it anywhere in the world.

Indians are afraid of it and so are white men. But as always, there are some white men who will "try anything once." The very fact that the Colorado is defiant is reason enough in the Caucasian mind to tame it. So far it is just about a draw. In the end, the white man expects to win, and so does the river.

The first white man to travel by boat on this stream was Hernando de Alarcón, in 1540, and he didn't have an easy time of it and he saw only a small portion near the mouth. Just who was the first white man to travel by boat in its upper tributaries is not possible to say. The first recorded journey was made by William Henry Ashley and party in 1825. Ashley was from Missouri and he wanted to be shown. He was.

Others followed, some unknown, some forgotten, until the formal exploration and scientific expeditions of Major John Wesley Powell, the intrepid one-armed veteran of the War Between the States, who completed a running of the unknown sections in 1869. Since then the challenge of the river has attracted many an adventurer and scientist. Some have never come out of the perilous canyons and rapids, and others have had dramatic success. To give in full details the hazardous story of each river expedition would be pointless and repetitive, yet no man who has ever braved the dangers of the stream should be slighted. For example, Buzz Holmstrom (whose given name is Haldane), with a quiet determination and an eschewing of all publicity, ran the river alone in 1937. It was an unparalleled feat and has been ably told by Robert Ormond Case in the *Saturday Evening Post*. Major Powell's expedition was the first to run the river; sixty-eight years later, Buzz Holmstrom was the first man to run it solo. Both achievements are river history. But between Powell's and Holmstrom's efforts there have been a number of expeditions for various reasons (or none whatsoever) which have become vivid stories in themselves.

Therefore, it has seemed best to present an account which would give the main emphasis to the variety of expeditions, and to mention in passing as many of the others as feasible. Personality and color determine the choice as well as history and science. The river has been run, or at least attempted, by an ex-governor, a major, trappers, miners, photographers, thrill-seekers, geologists, artists, criminals, botanists, a live bear, a bride and groom, and a madman. But to begin at the beginning there was Ashley.

Ashley

SPAIN'S sun had set in the Far West before 1800; and Mexico's never rose. A far greater orb completely eclipsed the red, white, and green; it was the red, white, and blue. The newborn Mexican nation of 1821 had only a confused idea of its northernmost lands, and only tenuous claims upon them. Roughly Mexico ended where Canada began, which was the California-Oregon border. Mexico, then, owned by right of first exploration all of Nevada, Utah, and Colorado, although only a small portion of this area had been visited.

The United States owned the area embraced by the Louisiana Purchase of 1803, and this extended from the Mississippi west "to the Rockies"—not a very definite boundary, but overlapping the Mexican claims in some instances. Actually, nobody knew who had what, and as late as 1825 men thought that there might be a river in Colorado that flowed into San Francisco Bay, and that the Great Salt Lake was an arm of the Pacific Ocean.

As the last flame of Spanish interest flickered and died, a new kind of frontiersman came on the scene. He was the trapper. The fur trade in the American West was a lucrative business and several vast American fortunes came out of it. Trappers appeared in Wyoming and Colorado and Utah. Some were Americans and some were French-Canadians and all were a hale and hearty lot. Some historians prefer the words "rough and tough." One hundred pounds of beaver pelts were worth from three hundred to five hundred dollars. If you were a frontiersman and knew your business, it was quick money. There was nobody to contest your right to hunt and trap in this virgin country. And who cared if the area belonged to Spain or England or the United States or the Arapahoes or the Blackfeet? Profits were the objective, and nothing else mattered.

William Henry Ashley was born in Virginia in 1778 and always had his eyes fixed on the West. He went to Missouri Territory when he was twenty-four years old and when the territory became a state in 1820 he became its first governor. But he was still looking toward the West, and hearing of the fortunes to be made in the fur trade, he went into the business with a partner, one Andrew Henry. Ashley was the power and the backing, and Henry was "in the field" in 1824.

Ashley himself came West in 1825 to look the land over. In the watershed of the Colorado and the Green River at this time were men whose names have become famous in the American West: Jim Bridger, Jedediah Smith, William Sublette, Jim Beckwourth, and David E. Jackson, for whom the Jackson Hole country of Wyoming is named. Ashley seemed to have a good idea of the type of country and the roughness of the frontiersmen, for along with his equipment he brought the first vehicle to roll on wheels into Utah—and it was a cannon.

Also Ashley brought business acumen. All of the French-Canadians who were in the area trapped for the Hudson's Bay Company, a British corporation. Hudson's Bay paid two dollars per pelt. Either Ashley, or his partner, Andrew Henry, convinced the French-Canadians that it was much wiser to do business with an American company. And it was not the cannon that was the persuasive instrument, but rather Ashley's willingness to pay five dollars per pelt. Even at this tremendous difference, Ashley could make a handsome profit, so great was the market for furs. The Hudson's Bay Company howled at this deal and called it a steal. Reverberations were carried to Washington and there nothing happened.

In the summer of 1825 a group of trappers met at what they called "the rendezvous" on the Green River in Utah, a tributary of the Colorado. Here they brought their furs and sold them to Ashley—furs that the Hudson's Bay Company was destined never to see.

While on the scene Ashley decided to explore some of this unknown country. With three boats locally built, the party began the first journey down the Green. Had they continued long enough this would have become the Colorado, and had they continued that long, none of them would have lived to tell the tale.

There were many beaver in these upper canyons of the Green and the Ashley expedition depended upon them for food. But suddenly all signs of beaver disappeared and the party found itself in a rushing current on a canyon-locked river and for miles there was no escape. They knew not what lay ahead as they continued downstream, their boats overturning in the rapids and their supplies lost or exhausted. After one day they realized that their plight was dangerous. On the second day it became desperate. There was nothing to do but go on for they could not turn back against the current and the sheer canyon walls held them as securely as any prison. For six days they endured starvation, and the French-Canadians decided to draw lots to see who should be killed and eaten to sustain the others. This horrified the ex-governor of Missouri and he begged the men to hold out one more day.

The gamble looked bad indeed, as the river cut deeper into the earth and the canyon walls rose ever higher. In Red Canyon where they were nearly wrecked by rapids so large they have been called waterfalls, the party halted by an over-hanging cliff. Here Ashley painted a record of the trip on a rock. It was a short-short story and no words were wasted. He wrote only "Ashley 1825." And the party went on.

If it was meant to be an epitaph it was premature. When all looked hopeless, and some were resigned to death, they came to a break in the canyon walls. It was a small glen, or park, known as Brown's Hole. Here they could leave the terrible river, but even at that they might all have perished of hunger had they not run into providential luck. Camped at Brown's Hole was Etienne Provo (or Provost), a trapper, who was well supplied with provisions and horses, and the perilous journey was ended.

Back in St. Louis, Missouri, and pinching himself to be sure that he was still alive, Ashley wrote an account of the trip that nearly cut short his career. He recalled the scene thus: "The river is bounded by lofty mountains heaped together in the greatest disorder, exhibiting a surface as barren as can be imagined," and he doesn't advise anyone to go boating on the Green. He did return to the river, however, in 1826 but looked at it only from its banks. That summer a great "rendezvous" was held, as Ashley brought many supplies from the East. There was much whooping and horseplay assisted by the firewater imported from St. Louis. Under the influence of these stimulants, enthusiasm and optimism blossomed and Ashley tactfully let it be known that he would like to sell out. And while most of the trappers celebrated, a young and alert group bought Ashley's share of the company. These men were Jedediah Smith, David E. Jackson, and William Sublette. Ashley wished them well and took a last look at the rendezvous and returned to Missouri. He was cured of his Western fever at last. In 1831 he was elected to Congress and he continued his career in Washington instead of on the tributaries of the Colorado. It was a wise choice for the fur trade collapsed in the early eighteen forties and finis was written to a little-known prologue to the history of the American West.

The trappers served their unintentional purpose; they opened the frontier to the emigrant and colonization. They left scant records. In fact, they were men of action and not of words. Ashley's episode on the river was almost forgotten, and years later, even as late as the twentieth century, men discovered the provocative and enigmatic message "Ashley 1825" and wondered who or what he was. And about all that can be added to the terse record is that he was a gentleman from Missouri who came first.

Powell

AFTER Ashley's abortive attempt to explore the West by river there were no other efforts that could rightly be called expeditions until 1869. The name

D. Julien
1836
3, Mai

is carved on the walls of Labyrinth Canyon, and it appears again much farther downstream in Cataract Canyon. There is no further record of Julien, and it is supposed that he was a French-Canadian, who, with others, went down the river to trap in unknown country. No doubt the river did the trapping, for no more was ever heard of the trappers. That they got as far down as the Grand Canyon before disaster overtook them is very unlikely.

John Wesley Powell was a studious young man and, at the age of twenty-four, deeply interested in the study of conchology. In this pursuit he worked for the Natural History Society of the state of Illinois. Few people were similarly interested, however, and as a conchologist had never been known to amass fame and fortune, young Powell's future seemed headed for obscurity and poverty.

Then came the Civil War and Powell volunteered and

became a major. But never during the conflict did he lose interest in his chosen profession. At Vicksburg he collected fossils from trenches, and from the Mississippi's banks he gathered river shells. Wherever his regiment went he studied the geology as well as the tactics of the enemy. At the battle of Shiloh in 1862 he lost his right arm. This tragedy would seem to seal the future of the young scientist, but Powell was made of stern stuff. His thirst for knowledge was never satisfied and he refused to be thwarted by adversity.

Mustered out of the service when he was twenty-eight, he married his cousin, Emma Dean, and the couple went to Colorado where Powell wanted to study the geological history of the West. At the headwaters of the Colorado he became fascinated by this stream.

By 1869, the general course of the river was known, but there were huge gaps that white men had still not seen. There were stories of all kinds—that it plunged over cliffs and created falls like Niagara, that it went into a cave and never came out, that it went underground and left boats high and dry, that it disappeared into the interior of the earth, and such poppycock. This was just the thing to appeal to the scientist. He would find out, traverse the river throughout its unknown portions, and publish the facts.

Toward this goal Powell gave the upper tributaries careful study. He understood at once the hazards of the undertaking, and he was, no doubt, the first man to challenge the Colorado properly equipped and with an appreciation of the power of his opponent.

The financing of an expedition of this type was not easy. Powell was unable to provide the funds himself, but he made a trip to Illinois and secured the backing of the Chicago Academy of Science and won contributions from lesser state institutions. In Chicago he had four boats built under his supervision. Three were twenty-one feet long and made of oak, and one was sixteen feet long and made of pine. This last was to be the scout, the advance boat, and was more maneuverable than the others. All had watertight compartments to make them unsinkable and to hold and protect scientific instruments. Ten men, including Powell, were enlisted for the adventure, and the Union Pacific Railroad, interested in the project, provided complimentary transportation for boats and men to the starting point, Green River, Wyoming.

At the start on May 24, 1869, the party was organized thus:

The small advance boat, *Emma Dean*, held Powell, John C. Sumner, and William H. Dunn. Sumner had been a soldier in the recent war and Dunn was a trapper.

The second boat, called *Kitty Clyde's Sister*, carried Walter H. Powell, a young brother of the one-armed leader; and G. W. Bradley, a sergeant from the Union Army.

The third boat, *No-Name*, carried O. G. Howland, who had been a printer; Seneca Howland, his younger brother; and Frank Goodman, an Englishman who had never been West before.

The fourth boat, *Maid of the Canyon*, carried William R. Hawkins, the cook; and Andrew Hall, a Scotch lad of nineteen.

All four boats were loaded with supplies in such a way that if any one of them were lost the others would still have a variety of all necessities intact.

The town of Green River, Wyoming, was a cluster of shacks beside the railroad in 1869, and there was little fanfare for the start of this expedition. The boats were cut loose and in a few minutes they drifted downstream and were out of sight. Unfortunately, the explorers had nobody appointed to the job of daily chronicler. Powell made notes but most of his story was written later from memory. Jack Sumner kept some notes on foolscap but these have never been published.

After incidental vicissitudes of the first few days, they came to a bad place which was more waterfall than rapids. On a rock overhanging the torrent they found that somebody had preceded them. Clearly somebody had painted the name "Ashley" and beneath it a date which time and the elements had obscured. It was 18-5, and they surmised that it was 1835, missing the correct date by ten years. None of the party had ever heard of Ashley, which is not odd when it is understood that the trip of the ex-governor of Missouri, made forty-six years earlier, had never been recorded. Later on, the party found traces of wreckage and decided this was the remains of Ashley's attempt. Powell wrote it up later with a pinch of imagination and describes poor Ashley struggling overland all the way to Salt Lake City and being aided by the Mormons and given work on the construction of their tabernacle. He never knew Ashley had been a man of means and a congressman. A pinch of imagination is sometimes more dangerous than none at all.

As most of the country through which they were to pass was unknown and many of its features unnamed, Powell showed a remarkable aptitude for nomenclature. Dozens of his names of canyons, creeks, rivers, buttes, mountains, and peaks were colorful and arresting and have remained permanent. Early in the trip Powell named the Canyon of Lodore for Robert Southey's poem "The Cataract of Lodore" and here the party had its first real taste of what lay ahead.

Powell, in advance in the *Emma Dean*, noted bad rapids downstream and signaled to the following boats to pull in for shore until they could investigate the danger. The two Howland brothers and Frank Goodman in the *No-Name* were a second late in obeying the signal. This was just what the river had been waiting for. Those in the *No-Name*, traveling at two or three miles an hour, suddenly found their craft sucked into a swift current and drawn by the unsuspected rush of water downstream at ten or twelve miles an hour straight toward the rapids.

Nobody could do a thing but watch while the men in the *No-Name* were shocked by the suddenness with which the river reached out and clutched them. Faster they went, turning sideways, then rear-end-to, and were slammed against a rock. The boat rebounded, careened, shipped water, hesitated, and then was swept again downstream through rapids at a rate of twenty miles or more an hour. A few seconds later, the *No-Name* hit a second rock broadside, and the impact smashed the boat in two halves as if it had been struck by a giant cleaver. The three men were tossed into the air and then plunged into the roaring, swirling torrent. They clung to pieces of the boat and were carried on for a hundred yards. Here more rocks and rapids smashed to kindling all that was left of the *No-Name*, and a bend in the river carried the survivors from the view of their electrified companions upstream. That was that, said the river. Would they like to play some more?

Fortunately, at this spot in delightful and poetic Lodore Canyon it was possible to scramble downstream over the rocks along the shore. By this means Powell managed to reach a point on the bank where he could see his three men. Goodman was clinging to a rock in midstream and the two Howlands had been thrown onto a tiny island. They were lucky to be alive. Of the *No-Name* there wasn't a splinter in sight. The problem was to rescue the men and not lose another boat doing it. The answer was found by the others controlling a boat from shore by ropes, and it took the combined strength of all to get the marooned men to safety. Of this, Powell wrote, "We were as glad to shake hands with them as though they had been on a voyage around the world, and wrecked on a distant coast."

That was the end of boating for that day, and the next

morning Sumner and Dunn went downstream to see if there was anything left of the *No-Name* worth salvaging. Their return was greeted with cheers for they had salvaged a three-gallon keg of whiskey which had miraculously escaped destruction and lodged between two rocks half a mile below. It had been smuggled into the boat and up to that moment Powell hadn't known there was any whiskey along. Powell named the place Disaster Falls, and by overcrowding the three remaining boats, the party proceeded downstream. The Howland brothers, battered and buffeted, weren't any too happy, and Goodman, chilled by his experience in the water, was morose.

They advanced for several days without major difficulties and reached the mouth of the Uinta River. Here it was possible, by means of a forty-mile walk, to reach the Ute Indian agency. This hike looked extremely attractive to Frank Goodman and he quit on the spot. No more rapids for him. What had been four boats and ten men was now three boats and nine men. And on they went into the unknown.

Their experiences followed the general events of those in Lodore Canyon. The river was always unpredictable and they had to be ever on guard. It drenched them with waves and soaked their food and spilled them overboard and slammed the boats into rocks and broke oars and gave them a constant battle. There were clear stretches of fair water but there was never any way to tell what was around the next bend. For all they knew they might come to a Niagara at any time. But on they went, naming their surroundings—Desolation Canyon, Gray Canyon, Labyrinth Canyon, Stillwater Canyon, Cataract Canyon.

Just below Stillwater Canyon, the Green River is joined by the Grand, and on early maps these two streams formed the Colorado. This is confusing to strangers to the Colorado who can't tell why there should be several names or which is which. It is a situation like that created by the joining of the Allegheny and the Monongahela to form the Ohio. In later years the name Grand was dropped, and it now appears on most maps that the Colorado River begins in the Rocky Mountains of Colorado and flows to the sea. The Green is one of its tributaries. Thus all the early river parties, except one, have had their beginnings on the Green and have joined the Colorado proper below Stillwater Canyon. It is all very arbitrary and manmade terminology. The Powell party was thinking up more specific names such as Hell's Half Mile.

After battling rapids and rising tempers and discovering a new prank of the river—to become so muddy that it is unfit for drinking—they noted a new stream coming in from the right. Sumner was ahead in the *Emma Dean*, and one of those following called to him, "How is she, Jack?" hoping that the new stream might be fresh and clear.

"She's a dirty devil!" Sumner yelled back. And thus the river was named. Subsequent attempts to change it to the more dignified name of the Fremont River have failed. A dirty devil it was and the Dirty Devil it remains, and it is an excellent and proper name indeed. In passing, it is worth noting that the Dirty Devil breaks up at its headwaters into three tributaries, and these are known as the Muddy, the Stinking, and the Starvation.

By this time the Powell expedition had lost all contact with civilization. The event had attracted national interest, and as stories of calamity are always more sensational than prosaic progress, a few newspapers printed unwarranted accounts of the expedition's collapse.

But the best racket of all occurred on a Union Pacific train. A weary and disheveled man boarded an eastbound express at Green River, Wyoming. Almost at once he started talking and he explained that he was the sole survivor of the ill-fated Powell expedition. Fellow passengers were interested and sympathetic. And the "survivor" explained how all the brave men except himself had been caught in a gigantic whirlpool in an awful canyon. The river spun them until they were dizzy and then a yawning hole swallowed the entire party, boats and all. The "survivor" had been on shore to investigate a side cleft, and had witnessed the horrible fate of his companions as they were sucked screaming to death before his eyes. He preferred not to talk about it any more; it was all too awful. He himself had lost everything, of course—but at least he had his life. The passengers commiserated, and one of the more magnanimous canvassed the train and took up a collection for this poor brave man. He didn't want to take the money, but at last he was prevailed upon to do so. And with that he quietly slipped off the train at the very next stop and was never heard of again.

An indignation meeting was held but it could do nothing more than express indignity. Where had this so-and-so said the awful whirlpool had drowned the men? At a place called Brown's Hole. But when the victimized got in touch with Mrs. Powell, they discovered that the party was far below Brown's Hole, for she had heard from them after they passed that spot, and that Brown's Hole was a small green park and the water there was the safest on the river. It is, in fact, the place where Ashley escaped. So some opportunist had made the most of his opportunity; and he was not, incidentally, Frank Goodman, who was the only man who had quit the party at that time.

The long stretch of peaceful water in Glen Canyon was a welcome respite. The three boats passed the Crossing of the Fathers without knowing it and at last reached the confluence of the Paria River. Two years later this was the site selected by John Doyle Lee as his hideaway. Lee called his place Lonely Dell, but it was even more lonely when the Powell expedition arrived in 1869 just ahead of him.

It was rough going from there through Marble Canyon, past the mouth of the Little Colorado and on into the mighty depths of the Grand Canyon. The loss of the *No-Name* and numerous upsets had played havoc with the food supply. And now they were locked in the granite vise of Grand Canyon and conditions were serious. They came to a small beach deep in the rocky fastness one mile below the rim. Here they rested and tried to dry their food. An inventory revealed that all that was left for nine men for what must be a journey of at least another two weeks to the tiny Mormon town of Callville far below Grand Canyon, was musty flour, some dried apples, and plenty of coffee. It was a grim prospect.

Rippling down from a huge side canyon, itself a scenic attraction had it not been dwarfed by the magnificent Grand Canyon, came a clear blue, sparkling creek. Its clear waters poured into the muddy Colorado and were quickly absorbed. Powell was far more worried than he allowed his men to know. He was, in fact, almost ready for prayer, and he recalled his Methodist father who had tried in vain to make a preacher out of a son born to science. Yet here was a situation that called for faith. While his men explored signs of former Indian settlements in cliffs adjacent to this pleasant little creek, John Wesley Powell gave a thought to his pious father and to his religious-minded namesake, and he called the little creek the Bright Angel. Standing beside its clear blue water, he said aloud, "And if this expedition has any right to success or survival, then listen to a scientist's prayer, O Bright Angel of Immortality."

On they went into country more forbidding than any they had yet encountered and the river, as if sensing their exhaustion, became more vicious than ever. The *Emma Dean* was thrown over a rock and landed upside down, and Powell, Sumner, and Dunn were tossed into the churning mess and battered and punched through rapids, half drowned in the muddy waters, and finally thrown onto sharp rocks. They managed to save the boat, bailed it out, and went on. It was all in the day's work, and that Powell, a one-armed man, could survive this speaks well for his endurance and nerve.

This was the heart of the Grand Canyon deep in the Granite Gorge of Archean rock. In later days Powell wrote vividly of the scene in a style somewhat flamboyant, but nonetheless accurate. He describes it thus:

There are cliffs and ledges of rock—not such ledges as you may have seen where the quarryman splits his blocks, but ledges from which the gods might quarry mountains . . . and not such cliffs as you may have seen where the swallow builds its nest, but cliffs where the soaring eagle is lost to view ere he reaches the summit . . . wherever we look there is but a wilderness of rocks; deep gorges, where the rivers are lost below the cliffs, and towers and pinnacles; and ten thousand strangely carved forms in every direction; and beyond them mountains blending with the clouds.

This is second-thought description. At the moment there was no time for literary musing. The whole party was too busy fighting a river which had only played before and now was really getting rough. Some rapids were impossible to run. The boats had to be carried—portaged—over the boulders on the shore. Where the canyon walls were sheer and there was no beach, as is often the case in the Granite Gorge, the boats had to be "lined"—that is, paid out on ropes controlled by those who remained at the last vantage point and these men would have to climb as much as a thousand feet in order to get over the granite and down to another beach just to do it all over again. Conditions of this kind plus lack of food brought tempers to the breaking point.

And then they reached a place that seemed to be utterly impassable. They made one portage and found that there was no way to make another. To run the furious river at this point looked suicidal. The drop was over a fall of eighteen or twenty feet, and immediately after that there was a second drop with jagged rocks below. They camped for the night and to some in the party it was the end. All that remained was to abandon the boats, try to climb out of the depths of the canyon, and walk toward the nearest settlements, Mormon towns which might be forty, fifty, or sixty miles away, provided they could live long enough to make such a hike.

Powell, however, would not give up, and he determined to explore the river until he reached the known lower section or die in the attempt. This meant another eighty or ninety miles. He outlined a plan for lowering the boats down the fall. O. G. Howland and Seneca Howland said it was foolhardy. For several days they had thought that Powell had been "touched" by the journey. Plainly, now, they regarded him as insane. They said flatly that they would go no farther down this terrible river. To do so was sure death, and they preferred to gamble on their chances of getting out somehow by climbing overland. Arguments were of no avail. And the mutiny gained a convert when William Dunn joined the insurrectionists. They were split six to three.

There was no sleep for Powell that night. He awakened O. G. Howland about two in the morning and they talked again. It was plain talk in the dark of that canyon bottom. Powell was counting on the Bright Angel; Howland could see only the Dirty Devil. The schism was final.

At dawn there was a tense and sullen breakfast of mildewed flour, dried apples, and black coffee. With three men quitting, a boat had to be abandoned by the remaining six. So they left the *Emma Dean* which had taken a bad pounding. The deserters took rifles and a shotgun but refused their share of the food, saying they could kill game on their journey. And with that they separated. What had started as four boats and ten men was now two boats and six men.

Miraculously, Powell and his men did get through what they called Separation Rapids and lived to tell of it. Bradley was nearly drowned and they all had hairbreadth escapes, but thirty-six hours after the schism, the six who chose to see it through were out of danger. They had emerged from the west end of the two hundred and seventeen miles of Grand Canyon, and they were in the comparative safety of Grand Wash. They were the first men to pass through the Grand Canyon and credit for this heroism is justly theirs. Some days later they passed the confluence of the Virgin River and just below that was the Mormon town of Callville. Captain Johnson and other men of the lower Colorado had ascended the river this far and now Powell had completed his journey through the unknown. It was August 30, 1869, just ninety-nine days from the time they left Green River, Wyoming. Brigham Young had advised the residents of Callville to be on the lookout for the party, but the Mormons had long since given them up for dead.

"The relief from danger and the joy of success are great," wrote Powell. "Ever before us has been an unknown danger heavier than immediate peril. Every waking hour passed in the Grand Canyon has been one of toil."

Callville is no more, and it is not possible to visit the spot where the expedition met civilization because the Boulder Dam has backed up Lake Mead and many feet of water now cover the site of the former Mormon town.

Meanwhile, the two Howlands and William Dunn had climbed the five thousand five hundred feet from the river to the canyon rim and this in itself was a worthy achievement. They were sure that the six well-meaning fools were drowned by this time and they congratulated themselves on their own wisdom. But Fate had a cruel trick waiting for them. They should, by all odds, have arrived at one of the distant Mormon towns; they were well on their way when they met some presumably friendly Indians. They camped for the night with the Indians, and later that night more Indians arrived from the north. They were all Shevwits, a branch of the Paiute nation, and the latecomers told of some brutal attacks by white men farther north. Indians had been ruthlessly beaten, killed, and their cached supplies stolen. A council was held and they decided that these three sleeping white men must be the culprits. The white men had told a fantastic story of having come all the way down the great river, and they were surely lying because no man, red or white, had ever done such a thing. These were bad white men and they must be punished. While the Howlands and Dunn slept, their fate was determined. Awakening in the morning with no suspicion that all was not well as it had been the night before, they filled their canteens at the spring, they were shot in the back without being given a chance to fight for their lives.

This story was a long time in leaking out, and it was over a year before Powell learned of the fate of the deserters. It was a totally unexpected outcome, but the Bright Angel had proved a better guide than the Dirty Devil. The fate of the three men might never have been known if Jacob Hamblin, the Mormon scout and frontiersman, had not unearthed it. He discovered Ute Indians wearing white men's clothes, and one Ute had a dented and useless watch. This property was identified as the Howlands' and the Utes had traded it from the Shevwits. Thus the Utes were exonerated, and the actual murderers were never found.

John Wesley Powell was not through with the Colorado River and the Grand Canyon. In fact, he devoted the rest of his life to it. In May, 1871, he made a second trip from Wyoming to the Grand Canyon. It was more leisurely and included many side trips and layovers, and was not completed until September, 1872. With Powell on this expedition were ten men, some of whom dropped by the wayside. One, however, was Frederick S. Dellenbaugh who later wrote two excellent books packed with detailed information, *A Canyon Voyage* and *The Romance of the Colorado River*, which are out of print and hard to find but well worth a perusal. They have become, along with Powell's report, the bible for subsequent river expeditions and are rich Americana from a nineteenth-century point of view.

Powell's work had attracted national fame. His energy and patience had filled in an unknown piece in the topographical puzzle of the West. He was to the Colorado River what De Soto was to the Mississippi or what Hendrik Hudson was to the river that bears his name. The town of Green River, Wyoming, is more than six thousand feet above sea level; Callville was less than one thousand. The river touched both and Powell discovered how and why and accounted for the terrain in between and especially devoted himself to a thorough investigation of the entire Grand Canyon area and much of southern Utah. Because of this vast experience in field work Powell was appointed by Washington as director of the United States Geological Survey. He and his colleagues and assistants carried out a detailed exploration of the Colorado River watershed in the eighteen eighties, and Powell widened his field to include studies in the archaeology and ethnology of the area. The wild guntoting West was gradually being taken over by the scholar and the scientist, and in 1894 Powell became chief of the Bureau of Ethnology, an office which he held until his death in 1902. Thus, a youthful and amateur collector of shells and fossils, in spite of physical handicap, pursued a brilliant career unparalleled in the history of the American West.

On the West Rim Drive of the Grand Canyon, not far from El Tovar Hotel and Bright Angel Lodge is the Powell monument. It commemorates in a few well-chosen words the first river expedition of 1869 and names the six men who completed the dangerous journey. Many tourists inspect it as they view the Grand Canyon from this point. Some do not know who John Wesley Powell was even after reading the inscription and explanation, and it is often taken as the marker showing the spot at which Powell "discovered" the canyon, which, of course, he did not do.

But the strangest commentary of all came from a party of three young ladies who arrived in the summer of 1945, all carefully decked out with the hallmarks of the dude—slacks and shirts and bandannas and cameras—in a mistaken belief that they would not be taken for dudes. They couldn't make the monument out. One of them said the Spaniards had discovered the canyon so this man couldn't have been the discoverer for who ever heard of a Spaniard named Powell? (General laughter, and the gag was so good that they repeated it at once.)

Then a great light dawned, and one of the young ladies said, "Oh—they went through on boats!"

The second, with a look of surprise which could have been no greater if she had been told they went through on roller skates, said, "Boats—in this country?"

"Not up here on the rim—down below," explained the first girl.

"Oh," said the third, silent so far. "Is there a river in the bottom?"

The carved face of John Wesley Powell, staring in grim determination on the monument, never smiled.

Brown-Stanton

T HE transcontinental railroads were spanning the country in the second half of the nineteenth century. The Union Pacific and the Central Pacific met at Promontory Point, Utah, and the last spike, made of gold, was driven in 1869. The rails linked East and West.

The Southern Pacific was completed to Yuma, Arizona, in 1877. The Atlantic and Pacific filled the gap between the upper Rio Grande Valley in New Mexico and Needles in California in 1883, and is today a part of the great Santa Fe system. This is the railroad that runs to the rim of the Grand Canyon today.

Farther north the Denver and Rio Grande Western crossed Utah and the Green River at the Gunnison Valley.

All these railroads were, of course, coal-burners, and coal was hard to obtain on the Pacific Coast. In this era of the rails, Frank M. Brown, a Denver capitalist, had a great idea. The solution to the problem of railroading is the grade—or better, the absence of grade. Mountains are the bane. Note the New York Central's "water-level route" from New York to Chicago. It is anything but direct, yet is the fastest and most efficient. Absence of grade is the reason for the route's success. Frank M. Brown decided that what succeeded in the East would succeed in the West. He declared that the answer to Western railroading was to find the "water-level route." The idea was a good one. It had only one fault. It wouldn't work.

In western Colorado there was plenty of coal; in California there was none. The coal had to be carried to the Pacific Coast. And Frank Brown found the way to get it there. It was simple and obvious and, if he hadn't thought of it, somebody else would have. It was a route made by nature. Simply start at Grand Junction in western Colorado and follow the canyon of the Colorado River. This gorge cuts its way deep across the American West through innumerable long canyons, one known as the Grand Canyon, and comes out at Needles in California. Nature had made this great cut following a gentle grade for man's ingenuity to use. Here was the Western water-level route.

This would indeed be a railroad's railroad to supply all the others, and it would only be a matter of time until it would be plain to the traveling public that here was the safest and fastest and levelest roadbed across the continent. It was foolproof—on paper.

A company for the immediate construction of the Colorado Canyon and Pacific Railway was incorporated. Brown was president of the company, and in 1889 he organized an expedition to survey the route.

One major factor was overlooked. In the bottom of this long chain of canyons was a wild beast that had never been tamed. With all the visualizing of a railroad in a canyon, nobody had thought of the temperament and character of the Colorado River. The time came when the river had to be considered. This dragon had never been saddled with a railroad; Frank Brown failed to saddle it in 1889; and it has not yet been done today. And as for that hindrance called Boulder Dam—well, the river is going to take care of that in its own

[129]

good time. In fact, in something less than a hundred years, the river will see to it that there isn't going to be a trace of—but this is about a boating party.

On March 25, 1889, Frank Brown and two of his construction engineers drove the first stake for the great Colorado Canyon and Pacific. It was a very expensive stake indeed.

Brown went East to attend to the multifarious business details and the first survey party started down the Colorado. This is the only important river expedition that did not begin on the tributary of the Green, although for all intents and purposes, it might just as well have. The first party went down the Colorado and up the Green, having a hard time of it as they ran out of food, but finally made Green River, Utah, where the Denver and Rio Grande crosses the state. Here they waited until Brown had made final preparations.

Dellenbaugh, in *The Romance of the Colorado River*, points out that time and again expeditions have run out of food. And the successors never seem to profit by this error, largely due to the fact that supplies are difficult to transport in small boats and the amount is usually underestimated in wishful thinking. Brown's party made this common mistake, and made many others as well.

On the twenty-fifth of May, 1889, Brown's expedition was ready to conquer the river. It never entered the heads, apparently, of any of the sixteen men who made up the party, that they could possibly fail. Powell had done it twice, and that was almost twenty years ago. Powell had four boats; they had six. They had his records and their expedition outmanned his. They didn't even bother to carry life-preservers.

Powell, and A. H. Thompson, a geologist and geographer who was on Powell's second trip, tried to explain the dangers and difficulties to Brown some weeks before his expedition began, but Brown never understood the hazards that lay ahead. With Brown was Robert Brewster Stanton, the chief engineer of the railway-to-be, and had Stanton been in authority over the president, it is probable that much of the tragedy might have been avoided.

Brown labored under the idea that six boats were safer than four and that there was safety in numbers. The river doesn't compute that way. Moreover, Brown's boats were all too small and too narrow, being only fifteen feet long and three feet wide. This type of craft looked fast and rakish and would have been ideal for an Adirondack lake. On the Colorado they had the seaworthiness of canoes in a typhoon. And not a life-preserver in the crowd. The river must have smiled when it saw this coming. The only explanation for such suicidal preparations is that Brown's thoughts were concentrated on his objective and he never understood that his every thought should have been devoted to besting the river.

Then the amount of luggage and supplies proved too heavy for the boats and when loaded they were down to the gunwales. To correct this, three of them were lashed together to form a kind of awkward raft. And this contraption carried half the supplies and all emergency accessories such as rope, extra oars, tools, and so on. Brown had expected these light boats to be maneuvered easily; but when three were lashed together, they were most difficult to control, and if anything were to happen to this improvised craft, half the boats and half the supplies would be gone at one stroke. Things were now beyond carelessness; they were stupid. And so they were off.

Through Cataract Canyon Stanton recorded seventy-five rapids, most of them within twenty miles, and waterfalls of sixteen to twenty feet. Within the first two miles they were in trouble. With bad rapids ahead, the raft and one boat went to one shore, and the other two boats to the other. Brown signaled to bring the raft over to his side. Since they were still half a mile above the roaring rapids, it looked safe enough.

But, halfway over, the strong suck, or undertow, caught the raft and pulled it downstream. The boat towing it could not pull it back. Slowly, sadistically, the terrible river was reaching for that raft, and gradually it pulled it toward the rapids. The tow boat cut the raft loose in order to save itself, and down went the raft, smashed, broken, splintered, with its precious stock either at the bottom of the river or its wreckage strewn for twenty miles along the canyon, while the party looked helplessly on. In two miles of bad water the river had halved the expedition. And still they would not learn.

Somehow they struggled downstream fighting the seventy-five rapids. By June fifteenth, three weeks after the start, they were still in Cataract Canyon and reduced to strict rations. One of the party made a gruesome discovery. He found the wreckage of a wagon and a human skeleton. No wagon could get within a hundred and fifty miles of the place where it was found, which meant that the ill-fated team and driver must have been swept into the river far upstream and washed all the way down. The skeleton had been crushed into the wagon box, and the whole thing was a grim warning. Even the river was trying to tell them to quit, but Brown would not.

Just below the confluence of the Dirty Devil it is possible to get out of the canyons. Later this spot became the minuscule settlement of Hite, Utah, a base for miners who later sought gold in Glen Canyon. Its population was usually three, sometimes two, and occasionally only one. There were two prospectors there in 1889 and Brown was able to procure a little food and a few supplies from them. The battered party rested a few days, and three of its members quit and walked out through the wilderness over the miners' trail to civilization. In the case of this expedition, what had begun as six boats and sixteen men was now three boats and thirteen men.

The work of survey for the railroad had gone on and Stanton was accomplishing his part of the trip in spite of the difficulties. The one hundred and fifty miles of Glen Canyon is almost all fair water. Brown went ahead to arrange for further supplies at Lee's Ferry and Stanton came more slowly, continuing the survey work. There was a long lay-over at Lee's Ferry while Brown went to Kanab, Utah, and back, for essential supplies. One more member quit at this spot, reducing the number to twelve, and on July 9, they began again.

The first of the vicious rapids in Marble Canyon was avoided by portage and the party spent a night at what is known as Soap Creek. Stanton later reported that Brown was in a pensive mood and could not sleep. He talked to Stanton about the project under survey and when they had exhausted that subject, Brown continued about his wife and children who were traveling in Europe. In the morning Brown was still in a disturbed frame of mind and he admitted that the strain of the trip was affecting his nerves. The river already had him and he sensed it.

In the very first rapid that morning Brown's boat was hurled over and over and the men thrown into the river. Brown sank into a whirlpool and was never seen again. Stanton, in the following boat, was on the scene a few seconds later and all that was left was Brown's notebook floating around and around in the whirlpool. The rest of the men were saved.

This tragedy ended travel for that day, and the others beached the boats below the rapids and deployed along the shore hoping to recover Brown's body. But the river never gave up the remains of the man who had thought to saddle it with a railroad. Darkness came and it was a lugubrious camp that night. Stanton now took charge of the expedition. To go back was impossible, to go on was perilous, to stand still was to starve. Under Stanton, the party, now reduced to eleven men, tried once more.

They battled the rapids of Marble Canyon for three days and were almost at the beginning of Grand Canyon when the river struck again. This time, instead of the leader boat, which was Stanton's, it took the second boat. Stanton and his men got through a particularly bad rapid with no more than a drenching, but the second boat was thrown against the canyon wall. It shuddered, cracked open, and sank. Two men, Peter Hansborough and Henry Richards, were drowned—Hansborough at once, and Richards after a desperate battle to swim out of the undercurrent.

This double tragedy was the end. Stanton surrendered and the river had won. The survivors sought a side canyon and found one at Vesey's Paradise, a cleft in the walls named by Powell for a botanist friend because of the lush growth in a small area. The miserable party now reduced from six boats and sixteen men to two boats and nine men huddled that night in the slight shelter of the cliffs while the canyon put on an exhibition of hell in the form of a terrific electrical storm. Lightning struck the cliffs and the rain came down in a cloudburst. Thunder boomed and reverberated back and forth through the sheer walls and the river rose two feet in a few hours. The schizophrenic was Mr. Hyde that night and his soul belonged to the Dirty Devil. The Brown-Stanton party never met the Dr. Jekyll personality or the Bright Angel. "Nowhere," wrote Stanton at a later date, "has the awful grandeur equaled that night in the lonesome depths of what was to us death's canyon." The next day the suicidal boats were abandoned and the men climbed out over the rim. By nightfall, in a state of exhaustion, they reached a cattle ranch.

Brown was dead and Stanton was defeated. But Stanton was alive to challenge the river again. He had implicit faith in Brown's scheme and he vowed that the Colorado Canyon and Pacific railway would emerge from a dream into reality.

Understanding at last the problems that confronted him, Stanton organized a new expedition, built stronger boats provided with watertight compartments, and had his men wear cork life-preservers. Then he tackled the job again, and after a series of typical river incidents, near-calamities, desertions, injuries (one member sustained a broken leg and had to be carried out of the canyon and up to the rim on a stretcher), smashed boats, and the discovery of the body of Peter Hansborough, they finally got through to Grand Wash. Stanton, and a few others, continued all the way down to tidewater where Alarcón had first seen the river in 1540.

At last Stanton had his survey and it was complete. All he needed now was to find somebody with the faith of Brown to finance and build the railroad. He refused to believe the project impractical, and for a man of his engineering skill and intelligence, this seems just over the mark into stubbornness.

The idea of a railroad following a watercourse is perfectly practical in cases such as the Hudson Valley and the Mohawk Valley. But to build a railroad in the bottom of the chain of canyons created by the Colorado is ridiculous for many reasons. First of all there could be hardly a mile of straight track without great expense; the sheer rock canyons would have to be straightened, cut through, tunneled, filled, and bridged. The river rises and falls at various seasons and the tracks, for safety, would have to be suspended in many cases well above the high water mark. Beaches and talus slopes and rock spills would be useless as roadbed, since the water sometimes inundates them by as much as fifty feet. And beyond all these natural difficulties there is not, and can never be, a single town capable of contributing to a railroad's support throughout the length of the canyons. It was all a pipe-dream that seemed practical only on paper, and a first-hand knowledge of the Colorado and its canyons called for the rejection of the plan.

And so the plan for the costly Brown-Stanton expedition evaporated into the rarefied western air. The Colorado Canyon and Pacific is now entombed in the graveyard of lost hopes. The river won.

The Amazing Kolb Brothers

ELLSWORTH and Emery Kolb came to the rim of the Grand Canyon and looked across and below in 1901. What they had thought to be the pattern of their lives was changed instantly. They didn't know it at the time, but the most important milestone of their lives had been reached.

The impact of the canyon on the consciousness of the brothers was no stronger, perhaps, than on many people. But, unlike many people, it registered just as strongly on their subconscious. It can be said that the Kolb brothers loved the canyon from the instant they saw it. They reacted to it with their intellects and their emotions; and they felt even more strongly the immense supernatural and mystic pull of this obviously natural phenomenon. It wasn't a case of their being unable to leave it; they simply didn't want to leave it. Others could come and go but they stayed on.

In 1901 it was possible to own property at the Grand Canyon, and the Kolbs built a house at the edge of it. They selected a magnificent spot at the very head of the Bright Angel Trail. The brothers were interested in photography and the house became studio as well as residence. It clings to the Kaibab limestone, a kind of aerie on the canyon wall. From any of its windows the view is breathtaking. As far as location is concerned there is no other house in the world like it.

And now that the Grand Canyon is a National Park and belongs to the people of the United States, the Kolb house is destined to remain unique. For a much longer time than is generally supposed, the Grand Canyon was not federally administered. That it should be is absolutely proper for this great work of natural art could not have remained in the hands of private or corporate exploitation, although few people realize that the area was not created a National Park until 1919. The transition from private interests to federal control caused a pinch now and then to property owners along the rim. A few islands of private land remain intact today within the park. The Kolb house is one and the Kolbs deserve the privilege.

From 1901 to 1941 the brothers explored the area. There never was a project too difficult for them and they ranged up and down the canyon walls from the Kaibab limestone at the rim to the Archean granite of the inner gorge, and from Marble Canyon on the east to Diamond Creek on the west. They knew as much of and about the Grand Canyon as anybody and possibly more. Remote sections that few tourists ever see, such as Thunder River and Cheyava Falls, were visited by them, and the Cheyava Falls were named by Ellsworth, at the request of the United States Geological Survey in 1923. It is a Hopi word meaning off-and-on, or intermittent, as it was first supposed the falls occurred only at certain seasons. Later it was found that they are permanent, but the name was not changed.

These falls are extremely difficult to reach and the Kolbs were the first ones there. It was a hard climb and a matter of going down the wall of the Supai formation hand over hand on a rope. A cave was discovered back of the falls and within the cave a lake. Until Ellsworth and Emery got there at the risk of their necks, this was an isolated part of the United States that no American had ever seen. And the difficulty of exploring this section of the Grand Canyon may be understood when the Kolbs explain that they first tried to get to the falls in 1908 and it was not until 1930, after several intervening attempts, that Ellsworth, lowered on a rope by Emery, set foot where no man had ever set foot before. The cave is sixty feet high at the entrance and six hundred feet deep. Today there is a trail from Bright Angel Creek to the base of these falls, and the average tourist considers even this too arduous an undertaking just to see and hear some roaring water. He has little or no concept of what the Kolb brothers have gone through in a labor of love to explore their pet waterfall.

Thus it is obvious that the Kolbs came to know the Grand Canyon in a way that no others did. They had their house and the canyon was their estate. In this demesne roamed a wild beast called the Colorado River. The brothers often came face to face with him. They respected him and he let them alone. They became distantly acquainted and they often snapped his picture. They got to like the beast, and they discovered that he had moods. He could be calm and placid and play like a kitten; or he could spring in bestial fury and ruthless cruelty like the inhuman thing that he was. They came to see that he had in his nature a dualism and that he was motivated always by one of two forces—that of an angel or that of a devil. And the transition from one to the other could be instantaneous.

The Kolbs came to resemble that Maharajah of India who, when told that a man-eating tiger was living in his park, said, "How courageous of him! But of course he doesn't know I am a man."

Emery says it was Ellsworth and Ellsworth says it was Emery—probably it was both at once—but each thought that they knew the beast well enough to try to ride him. Once this desire was acknowledged there was no way to overcome it. They would, sooner or later, have to have their experiment with the river. They read Powell's reports and Dellenbaugh's account of Powell's second trip. They noted the mistakes of the Brown-Stanton party. And at last they ordered two boats to be built and shipped to Green River, Wyoming. They resolved to add a pictorial record to the history of the canyon, and, since they were photographers by profession, they took along the first motion-picture camera to make the journey down the river.

Theirs was not the first attempt to follow that of Brown and Stanton. Nathan Galloway, a trapper, made several trips on the river, and two of them, one in 1895 and another in 1896, were from Wyoming to Needles, California. There were adventures but no casualties.

Also in 1896, George F. Flavell and a companion who is not identified went from Green River, Wyoming, to Yuma, Arizona, in one flat-bottomed boat. The trip received no publicity and has been forgotten. It is assumed that Flavell was either a prospector or a trapper. About all that is known today is that the trip was made successfully.

In 1907 three young men, Charles S. Russell, E. R. Monnette, and Bert Loper tried it in three steel boats. Loper's boat was wrecked in Cataract Canyon. Russell and Monnette took a severe beating, and the river got another boat in the Hance Rapids. Farther down, at Hermit Creek, the beast literally tore the third boat out of their hands as they were lining it downstream. The men climbed out and found help from Louis Boucher, the hermit of Hermit Creek (see later chapter, "Trail-Wise and Trail-Weary"). They located the smashed boat and managed to repair it well enough to get to Needles, but the expedition can be called only partially successful.

Julius F. Stone and a party of four (one of whom was the previously mentioned Galloway) left Green River, Wyoming, in 1909, in four flat-bottomed boats and made a successful run to Needles. This trip was remarkable in as much as none of the boats was badly damaged and two of them went through without a single upset. The beast was quiet that year.

Then came 1911 and the Kolbs with their motion-picture camera.

They decided to start from the farthest possible point upstream, where Powell began in 1869. This is Green River, Wyoming. Most expeditions have started here but a few have begun at Green River, Utah. For the sake of clarity it must be understood that on the Colorado's tributary called the Green there are two towns, each called Green River. One is in Wyoming and one is in Utah, and unless an expedition begins at the Wyoming town it cannot be said to have run the entire river.

On September 8, 1911, the Kolbs pushed off. They had a lad with them who could not stand the gaff, and after a few canyons and rapids, he unceremoniously quit. The brothers really didn't need him, anyway.

The Kolb boats were fairly small, but flat-bottomed which is important. They were very maneuverable, and the brothers perfected a new technique in running rapids. They let their boats go into the violent water *stern* first. This meant that the oarsman, with his back to the bow, was facing downstream with a clear vision of what was ahead. Also he was rowing, at the same time *upstream* against the current, which broke the downstream speed of the boat. It sounds very complicated but is ingenuously simple. The Kolbs had their upsets and near-drownings, but they had a great advantage over the old "hang on and hope for the best" attitude of earlier attempts. They were one up on the river to start with.

In Red Canyon they found a landmark. It was some paint on a rock under an overhanging ledge. It read only "Ash

[141]

. . ." and nothing more could be made of it. But history had caught up with facts by 1911, and the brothers knew that this was all that remained of Ashley's record painted on that rock eighty-six years before.

The river in 1911 was just as much of a threat as it had been back in Ashley's day in 1825. But in those eighty-six years some slight trace of the civilization beyond the canyon walls had crept in. Where nobody had explored below the Green in Powell's day, there had been trappers and prospectors and even escaping criminals by 1911. The brothers worked their way downstream and thought of those who had gone before under differing circumstances.

One of the most desperate cases in the river's history had been the flight of one Phil Foote and partner. Foote was a robber and a gambler and had tangled with the law more than once. He broke out of jail in Salt Lake City and, with his partner, fled to Green River, Utah. Fearing that officers were following him from the west, and that others would be waiting to intercept him in Colorado to the east, he stole a boat in Green River, and in the night he and his partner started downstream. They didn't know what lay ahead and they didn't care. Anything was better than the law.

Their boat, of course, went out of control and was smashed to pieces in Cataract Canyon. But the Dirty Devil was taking care of his own that day, and he caused the wreckage of a tent and some poles to be waiting on the rocks where the two criminals scrambled ashore. The canvas was rotten and there was no telling from what point upstream the river had brought this flotsam and dumped it there where two desperate men could find it.

They tore the tent into strips and made a raft out of driftwood tied together by the canvas. And on this insecure craft they sailed on. By all rights they should have drowned in ten minutes, but the devil carried them safely through Cataract

Canyon where it had cut the Brown-Stanton party in half. Unpredictable are the likings and moods of this river.

Still the convicts had no sinecure. The river might spare their lives, but it could not feed them. Days went by, and when the agony of starvation was no longer endurable, Foote's partner said he would plunge into the river and drown himself. Foote was a tough hombre, and such resignation to suffering enraged him. He said he would take pleasure in killing his partner instead. Whether Foote was motivated by homicidal mania or cannibalism it is impossible to say, but the partner decided he didn't want to die after all and begged Foote to spare him. In disgust, Foote did.

Later that day, they passed the mouth of the Dirty Devil River. For them it was a good omen. For a short distance farther downstream they came to the tiny settlement of Hite, and here Cass and John Hite were living at their base of supply for mining operations in the adjacent canyons. Hite has offered succor to more than one starving soul whom the river has brought to its shore, from a railroad president as in the case of Frank M. Brown to an outlaw and cardshark in the person of Phil Foote. The criminals were fed and, after a day of rest from their ordeal, they disappeared overland. Whatever happened to the partner is not known, but Phil Foote was incorrigible. Six months later he was quite properly shot and killed while holding up a stage in Nevada. He had roamed out of range of his protector, the Dirty Devil. Good sense should have warned him never to leave that river. It liked him.

With the story of Phil Foote in their minds, the Kolb brothers plunged into Cataract Canyon, rowing upstream but moving downstream in their peculiar technique of relativity. And to their surprise they came upon a solitary boatman. He was on shore and he saw them but gave no sign. He appeared to be a trapper and he had some coyote skins, a battered boat,

and no interest whatever in the brothers. In fact, his behavior was slightly antagonistic. And again they thought of
Phil Foote.

The brothers landed and prepared to camp for the night.
They introduced themselves and asked the stranger's name.
He hesitated and then said, "Why—ah—Smith."

He was of medium size and had but one light gray eye.
But he seemed utterly at home and self-sufficient in this
desolate spot. The brothers camped for the night a hundred
yards below the taciturn Mr. Smith but invited him to share
their supper. He said he had just eaten, but a can of pineapple
for dessert tempted him and the aloofness began to melt away.

Smith added Charles to his name and verified the fact that
he was a trapper. His boat was an old skiff that looked as if
it might fall to pieces if it were so much as kicked. But
Smith said it was a good boat. He had been through a few
rapids and upset a few times but accepted that as normal
river travel. The brothers told him of the danger and death
that lay ahead, but Smith was unimpressed. He said he didn't
mind the rapids as long as he could keep his tobacco dry. And
when he went back to his own camp the brothers noted that
he slept on his gun.

In the morning the relationship was still friendly and Smith
was given a short ride in one of the Kolb boats. He was
deeply impressed with the skill with which the brothers
handled the rapids. And he was able to be of great help to
them in running the motion-picture camera so that the film
would include both the Kolbs. Up until that time one of
them had had to take the pictures while the other performed
with the rapids. Since conditions were improving considerably, the brothers suggested that he come along with them,
but Smith thought about it and declined, saying that he was
traveling more slowly and that he wanted to stop and trap
at will. He also intimated that while his skins were all coyote,

there might be some others, and that his first reaction to the brothers had been cool for that reason. Then they understood. There were such things as game laws in 1911—laws which had been nonexistent in the days of Ashley—and it was an offense to trap beaver out of season and without a license. Smith, if not a poacher, was close to that status, and he had taken the brothers for a couple of game wardens. Now that all misunderstandings had been removed they were good friends. Again the brothers warned him of the dangers ahead and he promised to send them a postal card if he got through.

Cataract Canyon has always been one of the most difficult sections of the river, but the Kolbs came through in record time by conquering all of its vicious rapids in four days, a journey that took the Brown-Stanton party several weeks. Wherever the going was particularly bad they thought of the lone Charles Smith and wondered how he would fare. Eventually they found out.

Below Cataract Canyon they came to the Dirty Devil and like all others, they agreed that because of its muddy, sulphurous, odoriferous, alkaline water, this river was well named. They tried one taste and that was enough.

Below the Dirty Devil was the tiny settlement of Hite and when the Kolbs arrived the population was just one—Cass Hite alone was there to welcome them. He was an "old-timer" who had gone to California with the gold rush and had seen a lot of the West and a lot of life with it. He had many stories with which he regaled the brothers, and one of his favorites was that of "Sweet Marie." Those who can remember far enough back will recall that "Sweet Marie" was once a popular song. And the author, Cy Warman, believe it or not, wrote the song at the lonely spot of Hite, Utah, while the guest of Cass and John. The complete absence of "Marie" from the environs was doubtless the source of inspiration for the song, for Cass Hite told the Kolbs that only one woman had ever arrived at Hite in the past twelve years. "It's just not a female's country," he summed it up; the brothers concurred.

From Hite there are a hundred and fifty miles of fair water through Glen Canyon to Lee's Ferry and here the brothers had time for more than a concentrated fight for survival. They found many petroglyphs—Indian carvings in rock—throughout Glen Canyon and they wondered what the significance of the aboriginal art could be. These Indian drawings are pre-Columbian and are remarkably uniform in their execution throughout the American Southwest. Those on the walls of Glen Canyon depicting warriors, animals, trails, mazes, and seemingly abstract designs are essentially the same as those found in Nevada and in the Mojave Desert region of California. They are generally supposed to be about six hundred to eight hundred years old and are just as strange to the modern Indian as they are to the white man. They prove one thing for a certainty: the Colorado canyons were inhabited by an unknown race, which has since disappeared, long before most of Europe had discovered that the world was round.

Farther downstream the Kolbs camped at the Crossing of the Fathers and visualized the scene in 1776 when the Escalante party made its famous ford. And another day's run brought them to Lee's Ferry and the end of the quiet waters of Glen Canyon. From here on there were some very bad rapids: the Soap Creek Rapid which had drowned Frank Brown, the famous Sockdologer, and the vicious Hance Rapid. This was the very heart of Grand Canyon, but the brothers felt more and more at home. For high up on the rim above Bright Angel Creek were their relatives who were hopefully waiting for news. Theirs was the first and only river expedition to enter upon familiar ground with every increase in danger. A huge signal fire in Bright Angel Canyon carried the news to the rim that they had arrived safely; and the next day they cached their boats and ascended the Bright Angel Trail to their home one mile straight up. It was October 17, 1911.

But this was only an interlude. The ride on the beast's back was far from over. Some of the most dangerous sections of the river lay below Bright Angel Creek. The Kolbs took two months for a "breather" and then, resupplied, trudged from the snow-covered rim down to the river and pushed off once more. Two new men had joined them; another brother, Ernest, went a short distance, and Bert Lauzon, now in the Park Service at the South Rim, accompanied them all the way to Needles.

This section of the Granite Gorge is replete with thrills and hazards, and the brothers battled their way through rapids known as Salt Creek, Monument, Hermit, and Boucher. There were adventures every minute, but nothing could deter them and they were buffeted through swirling waters, razor-edged rocks and fifteen-foot waves with excitement and high spirits. Once a boat was badly smashed, but they repaired it on Christmas Day and continued on their way. They knew the beast now; they could judge a rapid by its very sound; they were professionals.

They passed Tapeats Creek and Thunder River, and reached Kanab Creek. Here Major Powell had terminated his second expedition, and from this point on the Kolbs had no literary material to guide them, but by this time they didn't need it. Later they came to the mouth of Havasu Creek with its sky-blue water gushing down from the home of the Havasupai Indians. It was zero weather on the rim and here they were in desert country of the lower Sonoran life zone with ocotillo and cactus in bloom. But the beast was not docile. He still had a few tricks to play. Lava Falls was one and here he was in such a devilish mood that even the brothers dared not defy him. They astutely "lined" their boats from the shore.

[147]

Eventually they passed Diamond Creek, the spot where Lieutenant Ives had stood and marveled at his first view of Grand Canyon in 1858. This is a section seldom visited by tourists as it cannot be reached from Grand Canyon village, nor does the water from Lake Mead extend up far enough so that it can be visited by boats from Boulder Dam. It is one of the wildest sections of the Grand Canyon country and was the scene of a tragedy of another river party at a much later date, a story of a honeymoon with an unhappy ending in which the Kolbs played the part of rescuers who came too late (see later chapter, "A Bride and Groom").

Very bad rapids are below Diamond Creek and at certain stages of water the worst section of the river is waiting for the unwary. Two lateral canyons pour streams in from each side, there is a sharp fall, below this a huge rock, and below the rock extremely vicious rapids. For the weary river-runner the Colorado has been saving not his aces—he has played all of those—but, here, the wild joker that means the game.

This is Separation Rapid, so named by Major Powell in 1869 when three of his party refused to go on. There is no way to "line" it; the river says, "Run it or else."

It was a battle but the Kolbs, battered and drenched, got through alive. There was little doubt now that a successful end was in sight. But the river wasn't quite ready to let them go; he slipped a last joker out of his sleeve. He dared the Kolbs to trump this one; it was an especially dangerous cataract. Wisely they refused his challenge. They made a last portage and declined his final dare. From that point on the rapids grew less and less severe and at last they came to the comparatively calm waters of Grand Wash. The battle was over; the beast was purring, and quietly he bore them downstream past the Virgin River, the ghost town of Callville, Black Canyon which now grips Boulder Dam, and on to the broad and calm water at Needles on January 18, 1912.

Powell had been on the river ninety-nine days and had quit at Callville; the Kolbs ended farther downstream, and their running time was one hundred and one days.

In the flood of excitement, exuberance, and satisfaction they opened their stack of mail. One letter, a surprise, delighted them. It was mailed at Hite, Utah, and it read:

Kolb Bros.

Dear Friends: Well, I got here at last after seventeen days in Cataract Canyon. The old boat will stand a little quiet water but will never go through another rapid. I certainly played "ring-a-round" some of those rocks; I tried every scheme I had ever heard of, and some that were never thought of before. At the last rapid in Cataract I carried all my stuff over the cliff, then tried to line the boat from the narrow ledge. The boat jerked me into the river, but I did not lose my hold on the chain and climbed on board. I had no oars, but managed to get through without striking any rocks, and landed a mile and a half below the supplies. I hope the movies are good.

Sincerely yours,
CHAS. SMITH

The brothers rejoiced. The odd friendship with Smith, formed under unique conditions, was genuine. Nothing could have made them happier than to know that Smith, too, had made it to his destination. In 1913, however, they received different news. A letter from John Hite told them of the death of his brother Cass. So the story of "Sweet Marie" would be told no more. And, sorry to relate, John Hite wrote that Charles Smith had made another trip south from Green River, Utah, that same year. All that was ever found was half of his wrecked boat. The Kolbs saluted the intrepid individualist with the words "a full heart pays tribute to the memory of Smith" in their own book called *Through the Grand Canyon from Wyoming to Mexico* by Ellsworth

Kolb. (Ellsworth later went from Needles to the tidal bore of the Colorado and hence the book's title.) For anyone who has lost his heart to the sport of running rivers, this book is a "must."

Their trip ended, the brothers returned to their studio, and developed the pictorial record of their adventures. But neither of them was through with the river and both returned to it, singly and together, a number of times. In 1923 Emery was chief boatman for another expedition of the United States Geological Survey. This party went from Lee's Ferry to Needles under the leadership of Claude H. Birdseye, and while it had its spills and adventures, it accomplished its scientific ends with great success.

But the 1911 trip of the brothers is the pictorial journey which they like to exhibit in their studio to the thousands of visitors who call upon them. The records are there today and are well worth seeing, and even if you have come only to browse in the studio and peer through the telescope and do not care to see the "movies," Emery Kolb will be there to welcome you. If he should choose to talk to you about the Grand Canyon in general, or any phase of it in particular, you will be privileged to hear an authority. You will be listening to a man small of stature and fastidious in dress, and it may seem incredible to you that this soft-spoken gentleman has tamed the beast that prowls the canyon bottom. But the longer you listen, the more you will understand that the Emery Kolb of the rim and the Emery Kolb of the river are two different men. He has secrets that he shares with the canyon and the river, and these are not to be heard for the asking. He is a twentieth-century Paracelsus who has touched both the alchemy and the mysticism of Grand Canyon and between him and this phenomenon are esoteric thoughts that he never quite puts into words. Perhaps there are no words to explain the transcendent meaning of both the Bright Angel and the Dirty Devil. Perhaps the full significance of this dualism steps out of space and time limitations. But Emery Kolb comes as near to understanding the behavior of the beast as any man. He has put his mark upon it, and it has put its mark upon him. Together they know something; be sure to listen for it; you could do no better.

Eddy

EXPLORERS WANTED

Volunteers are wanted for an important geological-geo-graphical expedition scheduled to leave New York City about June 10, to be gone six or eight weeks. Preference will be given to men who have had outdoor experience, and no one will be accepted who cannot swim, handle a boat, do his share of camp chores, and handle himself in the woods. No one should apply who is afraid of cold, or of high altitudes. A fine opportunity for geology students, or young members of teaching faculties, to do field work in virgin territory.

No salaries will be paid, but rations, transportation and camp equipment will be supplied. Each member of the ex-pedition will have to furnish his personal equipment, and will have to pay his own fare to the point where the ex-pedition leaves the railroad. In applying to join the party, state whether or not you are an American citizen.

Send photograph and complete biographical information in your first letter.

In the spring of 1927 the above advertisement appeared in university newspapers, fraternity papers, and on college bulletin boards. The person to communicate with was a Mr. Clyde Eddy of New York. Where Mr. Eddy's expedition proposed to go was a secret.

Interested?

More than a hundred college men were eager to learn more. Mr. Eddy sifted the volunteers down to forty and explained that the great adventure was a river trip down the Colorado from Green River, Utah, to Needles, California. At least half the applicants withdrew, and from those remaining, Eddy selected three young men from Harvard, two from Coe College, two from Notre Dame, and one from Northwestern. A ninth man joined the party through the American Museum of Natural History. A tenth was a cameraman. The eleventh was Parley Galloway of southeastern Utah. The twelfth was Eddy himself. And at the last minute a lucky thirteenth was added in the form of a tramp who joined at Green River, Utah.

This baker's dozen was an odd group. They were for the most part well-educated young men who had never seen each other before and who never intended to run the Colorado River, who were thrown into a group faced with daily dangers for six weeks, and who then separated and never functioned together or ever even met in a group again.

There was an impromptu, ridiculous, collegiate-prank aspect to the whole thing. Adventure beckoned and dared them; so they took the dare. Why not? What else was there to do?

The "geological-geographical" serious note never amounted to much. This expedition had no reason for being beyond the fact that Clyde Eddy wanted to go down the Colorado River by boat. In 1919 he had visited the Grand Canyon and had descended to the river at the foot of the Hermit Trail. The roaring stream caught his fancy and the germ incubated. He would not be satisfied until he had tried it. After eight years of incubation the germ became symptomatic. He had the river disease, and in 1927 he took the only cure: he ran the river.

The collegiate crew arrived at Green River, Utah, and became acquainted. Each of them would have given a reason for what he was doing, but none of the reasons would have been basic. They were not there for geology or geography or cartography or engineering or photography.

The real reason was that they had answered an ad tantalizing in its promise of adventure. Their spirits said—let's go!

On the surface it was all very mishap and misfit. But underneath it was well prepared. Clyde Eddy may have had a river-obsession but he was no fool. Three good boats had been built and carefully stocked. They were named the *Powell*, the *Dellenbaugh*, and the *Coronado*, after the river's explorer, recorder, and indirect discoverer.

At Green River the boys were warned of the dangers. "It's nothing—our boats are unsinkable," they replied. One citizen of the town said morosely, "In two weeks you'll all be dead." It was so funny they laughed in his face. Imagine any river stopping them! Who was this hick, anyway? Just a trapper who had been in the canyon country for sixty-odd years. What did he know about it? Let him go shoot a cat!

Eddy himself was older than his crew. He had served in France in the first World War when the rest of the party were playing soldier with wooden guns, but he was not lacking in the spirit that prevailed. It was all very simple and easy and later Eddy wrote casually:

On our last day in Green River a hobo asked me for a job. He told me . . . he had been a sailor. He professed to know all about boats . . . and had accompanied an expedition through the upper canyons of the Euphrates River and, therefore, knew all about rapids. I decided he might prove a valuable addition to the party.

I bought him a pair of shoes, a shirt, a blanket, and some overalls, and he joined us.

It was as easy as that. Anybody else want to come along? But the party was not yet bizarre and Eddy continues:

Knowing that a cub bear would be a picturesque addition to the party I brought one with me from New York. To serve as a mascot I had a dog which had been sent to me from the dog pound in Salt Lake City. The party was then complete, thirteen men, three boats, a dog, and a bear.

Certainly. And it wouldn't be complete without that dog and the live bear. Eddy continues, "The citizens of Green River turned out, to the last man, woman, and child, to see us off."

Of course. Who wouldn't? But they missed the camels, the giraffes, and the elephants.

All went well for a week; the river was too amazed by this strange party to do more than stare incredulously. Some odd expeditions had tried to ride the beast, but this one was the limit. The chap from Northwestern had a stack of blank paper. It was to take notes on, he said. A man from Notre Dame had brought a harmonica; he had figured there wouldn't be much to do while floating downstream day after day and he wanted something to while away the hours. A man from Harvard, majoring in English, brought a volume of E. A. Robinson's poems. And everybody was well supplied with cigars, cigarettes, and pipe tobacco. This was a cinch; all they needed were some co-eds.

They continued well on their way and one of their chief sports was to yell, "Hey, Ruth." The canyon walls echoed and re-echoed and the unidentified Ruth was paged all the way to the confluence of the Green and the Colorado.

Then the river caught the spirit of the thing. It began to play, too. It could not yell, "Hey, Ruth," but it had its own kind of fun. It decided to try drowning five of them. Wouldn't that be a lark?

The party had entered Cataract Canyon, and up to 1927 Cataract Canyon had taken the lives of almost one third of the men who had tried to run it. The Eddy party encountered its first rapids. It was a sobering experience and they battled through the first group, the second, and the third, with the going getting rougher all the time. Rapid number four was a vicious one, but Eddy decided it could be run. Their technique was that of the Kolb brothers: stern first downstream while rowing upstream. It was the best possible method, but just to make it sporting, the river was throwing up waves twenty feet high.

Two of the boats got through safely and were beached below the rapid, but the third, containing five men, went out of control and came through spinning and whirling and was sucked into the main current and sent downstream at thirty miles an hour into rapid number five. Undaunted, the cameraman continued to take pictures from this wild boat until the river reached out a wave and knocked him flat into the cockpit and took the camera away from him and sank it to the bottom. A few seconds more and the lost five were out of sight of the others.

They plunged through rapids, the boat filling with water, and the men rowing for life in order to avoid crashing into rocks. And, miraculously, after a mile, they regained control and managed to make the shore. That was all for that day, and the party was reunited by lining the other boats from the banks. A strong boat, quick thinking, youthful muscles, and refusal to stop fighting had saved five lives. The river laughed and granted them that round. The boys made light of the "incident," but they had learned a lesson and their attitude toward the river was respectful and guarded from then on.

The total day's travel was only three miles. Camp was serious that night.

The next day the river cut loose with everything it had. They were buffeted and whirled and soaked and spilled and smashed. It was the Dirty Devil at its dirtiest and it gave the boys plain hell. It played rough, it embraced no rules, it kicked and gouged and clipped and fouled, and its fury increased with every hour. It left the boys gasping and panting, bleary-eyed and groggy, and the river loved it. The total run after fourteen hours of hell was just three quarters of a mile. The boys had run a total of seven rapids; the river had exactly two hundred and ninety-three more in store for them, and all the really bad ones were still ahead. Come on, Harvard, Coe, Notre Dame, Northwestern! All-Americans, eh? So am I, said the river, an All-American from way back. There's the whistle; play is on; the river has the ball; he shifts, and pours through for a first down smashing boats, oars, and rowlocks as he goes. Great game, eh, fellows?

The boys called time out for the night but the river didn't know any rules. He played the game twenty-four hours out of the day. A dreary camp was made on a small beach. Thirteen drenched and bruised men, a waterlogged bear, and a bewildered dog tried to catch their breath. During the night the river rose and went after them. A flash flood came roaring down from upstream and the small beach was inundated. Still the water rose, and by midnight many supplies were lost and the boys were crowded back against the canyon's sheer walls and the river was swollen by a driving rain. At dawn the river fell a few feet, not enough to remove the threat, but just enough to encourage them to come on and fight. In the bleak gray light he showed them a new trick;

small rocks and large boulders, loosened by the rain, came tumbling and crashing down from the canyon walls. A direct hit would be enough to kill a man. While they thought about this a new day dawned; the river let them have the ball and went on the defensive.

The college team went into a huddle. It was a long huddle back on their own goal line. They came out of it slowly, grimly, fight written all over them. There wasn't a smile in the crowd. Forgotten were expensive sleeping bags, the latest waterproof ponchos, poems, notebooks, and harmonicas. Nobody called, "Hey, Ruth." This was do—or—die. This was fight and they meant it. Eddy called the signals and the team went into action.

Perhaps the most interesting contribution of this party is psychological. These young men were not obliged to continue this grueling ordeal. They were on a vacation. They had nothing to gain, not even a salary, by fighting for six hard weeks through to Needles. Life lay before them and the river offered nothing but a senseless risk of an early death. They had no obligations to Eddy; he had been a stranger to all of them. If not drowning, they daily faced the danger of injury, maiming, chills, fever, dysentery, and pneumonia. And all for what? Nothing. Nothing but the challenge of the river who dared them to fight or quit. And rising out of the psyche of all of them came the determination to see it through. They had asked for trouble and the river had hurled it at them. And now, by God, they would lick this river or the river would lick them. This was going to be a fight to the finish. Perhaps they were fools. But also they were youths. It was they or the river. Call those signals, Mr. Eddy.

This spirit is not new in American youth. It has been evinced before—and it will be seen again. America will never die until it dies.

Not everybody can sustain it. Some must crack. And

the Eddy party did not go through intact. After emerging from the battle of Cataract Canyon they had the one hundred and fifty miles of fair water in Glen Canyon and arrived at Lee's Ferry. Here there was a respite, while Eddy went to Kanab, Utah, for fresh supplies. By far the worst part of the journey lay ahead—such now-famous rapids as the murderous Soap Creek, the Sockdologer, Hance, Hermit, Boucher, Lava Falls, Separation Rapids, and the particularly vicious water at Spencer Canyon—to name only a few.

Four men left at Lee's Ferry. The first to leave was the last to join, the tramp who had fought the Euphrates and "knew all about rapids." He had caved in early, pouted, sulked, and belligerently quit. Bradley, the cameraman, also had enough. And two of the college men were forced to quit because of sunburn and injuries. Eddy advised them not to go on. They were both Harvard men; but the third Harvard man, the poet and student of English literature, went through to the end.

It is hardly necessary to recount the experiences of the party in detail from here on. It was simply a grim fight to the finish, and somehow the dog and the bear survived. At Bright Angel Creek the party rested again and Eddy went up to the rim at Grand Canyon Village and had a talk with that past master at running the Colorado, Emery Kolb. Kolb was extremely helpful to Eddy in describing in detail what lay ahead. Although the river is never the same at any two seasons of any year, the worst rapids are fairly consistently the worst, and Eddy was able to collect some advance information. This did not prevent their losing one of their boats in the Deubendorf Rapids. And at another time the dog was left by accident on a small strip of canyon-locked beach and the boats were moving rapidly downstream before the men saw him standing with his forefeet in the water and barking helplessly. There was no way to go back against the current and they went a mile downstream before they could find a place to land. Then back over the rocks, a hundred and fifty feet above the river, three of them climbed and, risking their necks, they managed to rescue "Rags" from the strip of beach. He was hysterically grateful, and by this slim margin did he achieve the status of being the first dog to pass through the Grand Canyon.

The bear, curiously enough, seemed to accept the journey as a matter of course and something that every bear went through at some time in his life. He was miserable most of the time and must have been a confounded nuisance as he was constantly breaking loose. Not to run away did he break his rope, but always to raid the food supplies. He was fed on boiled rice, pancakes, and milk, but he had a ravenous appetite and would eat anything he could get his paws on. He was only a cub, but grew rapidly, and his play was so rough that the boys named him Cataract. He and the dog got along perfectly but all of the men bore the scars of bear claws on their legs before they got to Needles.

Below their last rapid the men swam and sang and relaxed as they moved on downstream. There were no dangers now. It all returned to the "lark" stage. They had done it, and they had known all along that they would. Of the thirteen men and three boats, nine men and two boats tied up at Needles on August 8, 1927. There had been no fatalities. Now that the party was about to break up there was a desire to "do it again." Several of the boys urged Eddy to plan a new trip on the spot. They were a wild-looking lot, unshaven, half naked, and with what clothes remained in tatters—but they were happy.

"Let's run the Yukon," somebody suggested, and "I hear the Mackenzie is supposed to be tough—how about it?"

But Eddy was through. He had conquered his river fetish. The Colorado had been successfully run. He had had enough.

He gave the dog to one of the boys and the bear was sold to a Santa Fe Railway engineer. The party dissolved and the nine men went their separate ways; they have never met as a group since.

Eddy wrote the whole trip in detail into a book; it would interest anybody who wanted to run the river. The London edition is called accurately enough *Danger River*, and the subtitle reads, "Being an account of the only successful attempt to navigate the rapids of the world's most dangerous river." That was laying it on pretty thick. Somebody overstepped in writing that line, but it may have been a last-minute thought of the publisher rather than of Clyde Eddy. At any rate, it stands corrected, and it is to be hoped that if there is another edition of *Danger River*, the subtitle will be changed to: "Being an account of the only attempt to navigate the rapids of the world's most dangerous river with a mongrel dog and a live bear for no reason at all."

A Bride and Groom

THIS is a happy story with a sad ending. Or perhaps it has mystic or symbolic or hymeneal overtones which lift it entirely from the plebeian values of happiness and sadness, of pleasure and pain, of dualistic ephemeral nature.

Glen R. Hyde was in love.

All the world, it has been written by a sage, loves a lover. Glen Hyde, however, had two loves. One was the girl of his dreams and the other was rivers. He had made a careful study of irrigation; that was the business aspect of rivers. And he had made three important river conquests of running and exploration; that was the sporting aspect of rivers. His three victories included the successful running of the Salmon River in his native state of Idaho, and of the Fraser and the Peace Rivers in Canada. By that time he knew all the tricks. But there was one river he was longing to conquer and that was the Colorado.

At the age of twenty-eight, Glen decided that it was time to marry. He was in love with a pretty girl of twenty-four whom he had met in college. She was from Parkersburg, West Virginia. He had told her, Othello-like, round unvarnished tales of his conquest of the Salmon, the Fraser, the Peace, and his stories won his Desdemona.

But there was one more river, and he wanted it. It had

been run before and the score was about fifty-fifty. Still, he was sure that he could conquer this river. He had his own method. Always before men had attempted it in boats of the skiff type. And they were tossed and smashed more often than not. Glen had invented the perfect boat to whip the Colorado. It looked cumbersome but was not; it looked awkward but was readily maneuverable; it looked like a scow but it had the speed of a ketch. He wanted to build this boat at Green River, Utah, and run the Colorado. He wanted to marry the girl and take her with him on a honeymoon. Would she accept his proposal?

She did.

And so, in October of 1928, they were married.

Glen built the boat himself, for he knew exactly what he wanted. It was twenty feet long, five feet wide, and three feet deep. It had two eight-foot bladed sweep oars at bow and stern, and the trick was for Glen to stand amidships and operate both oars at once. This gave him full control of the boat at all times in all kinds of water—or so he said. No other oars for propelling were necessary. This was purely a river boat and would conquer any river.

Mr. and Mrs. Glen R. Hyde were very happy. They began their honeymoon trip on October 20, 1928, and they rejoiced as they dropped quickly downstream and the town of Green River, Utah, was soon out of sight. The honeymooners were alone, and they would be alone for many weeks while traveling through the most remote and desolate country in the United States. It was the highest moment of Glen's life; he had his river and he had his bride.

The ketch that looked like a scow completely vindicated its designer's faith. The run from Green River, Utah, to Bright Angel Creek was made in twenty-six days. This is very good time indeed when you recall that Cataract Canyon not only retarded, but annihilated many a party, and that the Soap Creek and the Sockdologer and the Hance Rapids were also lurking along the way, not to mention many others.

On November 15, Mr. and Mrs. Hyde moored their scow at the spot where Major Powell had appealed to the Bright Angel, and ascended to the South Rim of the Grand Canyon. And here they called at the Kolb Studio and had a long talk with Emery Kolb. He was amazed at their success and the speed of their trip, and they confided that often, in order to make record time, they cooked and slept in the boat.

Glen was quite confident that he would tame the Colorado, although he admitted that there were times when the previous rivers he had run seemed mild in comparison to this one. He stated that the trip was purely personal, that he had no scientific interests beyond proving that his type of boat was the answer to river-running, and that he wished to give his wife a thrill. Why, just think, in another two or three weeks, she would not only be the first bride to make the canyon voyage, but she would be the first woman in history to ride the Colorado River. They looked at each other and smiled.

Emery Kolb had a moment of trepidation. Had the beast thought of this, he wondered. Was it going to be an angel about it, or was the devil grinning and waiting. He knew this river too well. It had been all too easy with that scow and its eager twosome crew. What did it mean? Twenty-six days from Green River, Utah, to Bright Angel Creek. That was not like the river that Emery Kolb knew; he sensed duplicity. Something was going to happen, something that these happy bright-eyed people might not suspect.

"Of course," he said, trying to make it casual, "you are carrying life-preservers?"

"No," said Glen. "Now about Separation Rapids, I understand that there is a—"

"No life-preservers *at all?*" asked Emery slowly.

"Don't want 'em," said Glen.

"But haven't you been spilled overboard or pulled into the river at any time?"

"No—no—" said Glen, discounting the importance of these tangent remarks.

"Oh, yes," said his wife. "Once—in the Sockdologer Rapids —don't you remember, Glen?"

"Oh, that," said Glen. "That wasn't anything. I slipped— that's all."

"And I just did get a rope to him in time," she said wistfully to Emery Kolb. "He barely caught the end of it."

Emery Kolb was studying them carefully. He had listened to their story with interest, but his mind was turned to the river. He was hearing its roar, its crashing rapids; he was letting his intuition function. He was trying to read the beast's mind. And the beast spoke to him then and there. It permitted him to visualize a scene that was not pleasant. It was only a flashing second, a quick visualization, but it stirred Emery into action.

"You must have life-preservers," he said, rising and pacing across the room. He stood with his back to the Hydes and stared out into the depths of Grand Canyon. Far across the abyss was Bright Angel Creek. And down there in the bottom was that scow, and lapping beside it was that river. He turned back to his guests. "You must have life-preservers," he reiterated. "I have some; I'll give you mine."

He watched the Hydes. Their expressions changed. A trace of a frown passed over Glen's face.

"We don't need them, Mr. Kolb," he said calmly.

Again Glen and his wife looked at each other. They both smiled as if they shared a secret, and then they looked politely back at Emery Kolb. And Emery knew then what the story would be, and there was nothing he could do about it. Only he and the river knew that each had had a glimpse into the future. And all that there was to do was to let destiny catch up to that future moment and play its scene.

Still Emery would not give up. Perhaps these were marked children floating downstream until the river had prepared an altar of sacrifice, but there was still time; they might yet be dissuaded. He exhorted them to take his advice. He could not ask them to give up the trip for they would think him crazy. But if they would not accept his life-preservers and cork life-belts, would they not at least walk the few yards to the Fred Harvey garage and buy or borrow some inner tubes? These were not as good as life-belts, but they would do in an emergency. Would they please do that?

Glen said they would—of course, they would—and about Separation Rapids. . . .

And the talk went on.

The next day the Hydes were ready to descend to their boat. Emery Kolb's wife and daughter went with them to the head of the trail. There everybody stopped for a brief good-bye. Glen was ecstatically happy. The second half of the trip was about to begin. If it turned out as well as the first half they might set all kinds of canyon records. But Mrs. Hyde was quiet. Something had registered in her woman's intuition: some message, some mood, some warning. Had she picked it up from the talk with Emery Kolb—or was it from the river? She could not say, but she knew something that her husband did not yet know. She was his bride, and yet, the river had never taken a woman to its bosom. She was the wife of Glen Hyde and she would go wherever Glen Hyde went—and yet, there was another bridegroom waiting. She was the first to tempt the beast. Would he want her? Already she knew. It was something about which it was not possible to be articulate at that moment. She wanted to say, "Glen, let's not go any farther. Let's give it up. Let's never go down to that river again!" But he would not understand. He wanted her to go, and so she must. He was starting down the trail and calling farewells and thanks to the Kolbs. She wanted to say something nice to them, too, but all she could think was, "I don't want to go, I don't want to go."

She looked down at her feet. They were encased in heavy hiking boots. And Mr. Kolb's daughter was wearing such smart new shoes. She caught her breath and looked up. "I wonder," she said to the Kolbs with a smile, "if I shall ever wear pretty shoes again." And she turned and followed her husband down the trail.

That was November sixteenth.

The Hyde's method of keeping track of the days was very simple. They cut a notch for each day on the gunwale of the scow with a cross for every Sunday. And Mrs. Hyde kept a brief diary with dots indicating rapids and dashes for the quiet stretches in between. Occasionally she made notations in the diary, such as "November 17, left Bright Angel Creek."

On the eighteenth she recorded, "Left Hermit Camp." On the twenty-second, "Passed Tapeats Creek." On the twenty-fourth, "Smashed a sweep oar. Glen repaired it." And on the thirtieth, "Ran sixteen rapids today."

Thus it can be seen that they were doing very well indeed. They had conquered most of the rapids; they were nearing the western end of Grand Canyon; and there were forty-two days recorded on the gunwale. It looked as if they might break the record. There remained only Lava Falls, Separation Rapids, and Spencer Canyon. After that they would be in the calm waters of Grand Wash and victory would be theirs with a triumphant journey on to Needles and the most unusual honeymoon in the world would be over.

Up on the rim of Grand Canyon everyone was wishing the

Hydes the best of luck. No news had come from them, of course, and there couldn't be any before mid-December at the earliest. Any time after that date they might be expected to emerge from the chain of canyons. There was no Boulder Dam in 1928 to shorten their journey, but on the fifteenth of December those who had followed the expedition began to look for word.

Christmas came and still there was no news. They should have been in civilization by that time. Something must have delayed them.

December went by and 1929 came in. It began to look serious. And after the first week of January had gone by, it *was* serious. The only report was "Overdue at Needles."

Mid-January came and then everybody knew that tragedy had struck. Somewhere in the canyons the Hydes had vanished. But all anybody could say was the meaningless "Overdue at Needles."

Then Glen's father arrived from Idaho to instigate a search. But how and where to search? All the father could do was to stand at the head of Bright Angel Trail and wonder where in that great gorge were his son and daughter-in-law. He appealed to the Park Service, to the United States Army, and lastly to Emery Kolb.

Emery Kolb had gone to Phoenix to a hospital to have an appendectomy performed. But as soon as he received the elder Hyde's plea he postponed the operation and hurried back to Grand Canyon. There is a curious sidelight to this. For Emery Kolb has not yet had the appendectomy and, while he was part of a searching party, his doctor, who had declared the operation imperative, died.

Meanwhile the United States Army had gone into action. Lieutenants Adams and Plummer of the March Field Air Base in California flew over the canyon country the length of the lower river in a single-motor six-hundred-horsepower Douglas. Deep in the lower Granite Gorge they sighted a boat. It seemed to be stationary in the middle of the river. They brought the Douglas down at Grand Canyon airport.

But nobody could be sure that this had been the Hyde boat. Only Emery Kolb knew enough about the scow to be able to recognize it from the air. And at the insistence of the two lieutenants and the elder Hyde, Emery Kolb, presumably ready for hospitalization and a serious operation, bundled himself up in a flying suit, braved the zero weather in an open cockpit ship, and flew with Adams to the unidentified boat.

Describing this trip, Emery says:

In going over the canyon Adams flew the ship as if it were an eagle, swooping and diving over the peaks. And when he arrived at the scene he dived like a bullet into the inner gorge just over the boat. He passed back and forth many times so that I could get a good view, and instead of climbing out of the narrow gorge to the wider plateau, or Tonto Bench region, he would bank up sideways and make the turn in the inner gorge. The cold wind got by my goggles and my eyes were streaming. My clothes were so heavy that I loosened the safety belt so that I might turn around far enough to get a good view of the boat. Adams saw that I was having difficulty, and not knowing that I had loosened my belt, turned sideways right over the boat and nearly dumped me out. But I was able to determine without any doubt that the craft below was the Hyde boat. There was no sign of life. In the dark we returned to Grand Canyon airport.

The next morning an expedition set out to reach the boat. It consisted of Emery Kolb, Chief Ranger Brooks, M. J. Harrison of the National Park Service, and the elder Hyde. They followed the highway south to Williams and west to Peach Springs. Here Kolb and Brooks walked the twenty-two miles to the river at Diamond Creek, the exact spot at which Lieutenant Ives had first seen the Grand Canyon in 1858. Harrison and Hyde went with supplies by wagon.

At the mouth of Diamond Creek there was an old flat-bottom boat which had been used twenty years previously by a mining company. It was rotten and full of holes. Brooks and Kolb found some old canvas and with the few supplies that arrived by wagon, completely reconstructed the boat. Emery had wired his brother Ellsworth who was in Los Angeles, and, drawn by the same irresistible force as that which played upon Emery, Ellsworth turned up at the mouth of Diamond Creek in time to help finish the boat. The following morning Ellsworth, Emery, and Chief Ranger Brooks pushed off. Again the brothers were riding the beast, and this time in a cockleshell boat that soaked up water like a sponge.

Fourteen miles below Diamond Creek and two miles above Separation Rapids they came to the scow. It was right side up, had shipped a foot of water, and was securely held by its own rope which had caught on the river bottom. So firm did the rope hold that it had to be cut in order to release the scow. The two sweep oars were in working order and all bedding, clothes, food, and utensils were in place. The rescue party salvaged what equipment they could, including Mrs. Hyde's diary, a gun, and a copy of the Kolbs's own book which the Hydes had used for a guide. There were forty-two notches cut into the gunwale so the rescuers could figure to the day when the last record had been made. Moreover, there was the diary. These facts left no doubt that the Hydes had disappeared on December 1, 1928—or more than seven weeks before.

In spite of the tragic mood that prevailed, Ellsworth could not resist a try at this strange craft. He ran the waterlogged scow over a rather bad rapid and reported that the two sweep oars were so perfectly balanced that a child could operate them. It had not been their boat that had failed the bride and groom.

It was impossible for the rescue party to return upstream to Diamond Creek in their old boat. They had foreseen this and had arranged to have horses meet them farther downstream at Spencer Canyon. But in order to get there they had to run Separation Rapids in their old tub. This was as hazardous as any experience the brothers had yet had on the river. It was impossible to control the old boat and one sound crack against a rock would mean the end of it. As it was they had a nasty spill in Separation Rapids and Chief Ranger Brooks was nearly lost. Then, in frozen clothing, they traveled six miles to Spencer Canyon where they were met by a party sent on ahead with Walapai Indians and horses. This kind of thing will either kill or cure a man with appendicitis, and happily, in the case of Emery Kolb, he was cured.

Meanwhile, those left at Diamond Creek had worked upstream in an attempt to find any trace of the Hydes in that direction. The last place their tracks appeared was seven miles upstream above Diamond Creek. Thus twenty-one miles separated the last trace of the bride and groom and their scow. What had happened to them?

There are three or four suppositions, and each is a guess as good as the other. Emery Kolb thinks it is likely that they were trying to "line" their scow over bad rapids, and the heavy boat pulled them into the river and they were drowned. Another theory is that they had landed on a canyon-locked beach and a flash flood came downstream and took the scow with it, leaving them to starve. Another is that a sudden jolt or shock threw them both out of the boat into the river, though this last is unlikely as there would have been no dragging rope under those circumstances, and furthermore, such a bump would have upset the orderly arrangement of their effects within the boat.

But nobody really knows. Only the river can say what happened to the bride and groom. It is to be hoped that the beast was merciful and took them unto himself quickly and together. But it is possible that he disposed of the man first, for he was not interested in him, leaving the girl on a strand of beach. It is not a pleasant thought. For either she had a slow death of exposure and starvation, or the river rose, slowly and inexorably, and claimed his bride.

The Hyde case has been used by the Park Service as a warning. Pleasure trips on the Colorado are discouraged, and the government insists that no such expeditions be attempted except in the interests of science and insists that even these be accompanied by experienced rivermen with the best possible equipment.

But this is not the answer. The Hydes were well equipped and the scow was a capable craft. They had almost made it and by all odds they should have come through successfully. The Hydes are not to be blamed. It was the river. Nobody thought in advance that the beast had never seen a girl before, that he would study her for a long time, and that finally he would take a wife.

White

After all the fanfare and honors and plaudits had been spent on the heroes of the Colorado River, the inevitable argument came out of its hiding place and a question was posed. That great bugbear, doubt, entered the picture.

Who was the first man to conquer the Colorado River and pass through the Grand Canyon? Who gets the credit, the honor, the glory? And all the heroes from Major Powell to Buzz Holmstrom had the props pulled out from under them by a small and loyal band who insisted that all of the adulation heaped upon the brave, from Powell to Holmstrom, inclusive, was misplaced. Powell, this clique insists, was not the first man to run the river, nor was Holmstrom the only man who ran it alone. That double honor, they declared, is reserved for James White.

And who is James White?

He was a young man from Kenosha, Wisconsin, who went west in 1865, and who, in 1867, two years before Powell, ran the Colorado alone. At least that is the claim on the part of White's adherents. The story, from White's point of view, is simple and harrowing, but a great many claims and counterclaims have since cluttered it up. Poor James White did not know what a mare's nest he was destined to expose. He was a simple ignorant prospector and the fact that his adventures led to long and bitter arguments for more than fifty years, reaching a climax with vindicatory forensics in the United States Senate, was a great surprise to him. After all had been officially done and recorded, he was pushed forward with the claim that he had done it first. It became a bitter farce, and to the general public it was something in the nature of the argument that it wasn't Homer who wrote Homer's poems at all, but another man by the same name.

But White's story is not fiction. Only in the final interpretation was there error. White began by telling the truth and what is more he stuck to it. Here is what happened to him:

After a start, which he admitted began by stealing horses from Indians, he arrived with three friends in Colorado. There was some dissension about who had title to the stolen horses, and in a fight White shot one of the party. The wounded man was left behind and the others including White, three in all, pushed on to southwestern Colorado. From there they traveled through unknown country. None of them had any knowledge of the geography of the Southwest, but that didn't bother them. They were rough frontiersmen looking for gold and they wanted to get into a land as untouched as possible.

They knew that they followed the Mancos River out of Colorado into New Mexico near the only place where four states come together at a point: Colorado, Utah, New Mexico, and Arizona. From there on they traveled southwest into Arizona, but just how far White was unable to say. As they were prepared for a long trip, it must have been a considerable distance and White's estimation was anywhere from sixty miles to two hundred and sixty.

He did not know the first name of one of his companions and called him simply Captain Baker. The other man was George Strole. They were in canyon country. At one time White thought he saw an Indian but the others were not apprehensive. The following day they were ambushed by

Indians. Captain Baker, who was in the lead, was shot dead, the bullet passing through his heart. White and Strole fled in panic down a box canyon. They abandoned their horses, believing the Indians might find the animals and stop to capture them rather than pursue two white men. After a journey of what seemed to be fifteen miles, they came to the mouth of the canyon, and here it joined another and larger canyon in which there was a surging river. It was sunset, and White and Strole, fearing pursuit, built a raft of cottonwood logs, which they lashed together with their lariats, and pushed off downstream in the dark. They had no idea where they were and all that was imperative was to escape the Indians.

White thought, in retrospect, that they traveled four days on smooth water and he recalled that they sat on the raft and dangled their feet in the river. Rations were low as they had been able to carry little food during their flight. Then they came to a small rapid which tipped the raft over and White was saved from drowning by Strole who held him by the hair of his head.

They camped at night and the next day continued floating downstream as there was no other means of escape. The canyon walls were sheer and composed of yellow sandstone, and this fact White swore to many times in later questioning. It was a most important point.

That day they came to furious rapids with falls of fifteen feet, and George Strole was pitched off the raft and drowned while White looked helplessly on. In order to save himself, White lashed himself to the raft.

Then followed an indeterminate number of days (White thought fourteen days altogether were the total number he spent on the river) during which the raft was tossed and smashed and White expected every moment to be his last. He declared, however, that there were no more bad rapids like the one in which Strole was lost, but that there were many lesser ones and that once the raft was caught in a whirlpool and went spinning round and round for two hours. White, who never in his life had prayed, then resorted to a plea to God to save him, and shortly after that, the raft was freed from the whirlpool and continued downstream.

By this time White was in a famished condition and by good fortune he met some Indians who waded out from shore and pulled him to land. He declared that there were seventy-five of them, which seems unlikely at that spot, and that an old squaw gave him some mesquite bread. He knew that one was a Walapai (how he could know this when he had never heard of Walapais he never said) and that the rest were Utes. When they would give him no more food he returned to his raft and went on down the interminable river.

He insisted that there were no more rapids. His condition, however, was serious. Most of his clothing had been torn or worn to shreds and he was suffering from sunburn and blisters.

A day later he met more Indians and traded them his revolver for the hindquarters of a dog. At the Indians' camp-fire, he cooked one quarter of dog and ate it. He slept beside his raft and in the morning he pushed off again, with the remaining quarter of dog for breakfast.

After another day he was in such a starving condition that his mind wandered. The sunburn was constant torture and he suffered from boils. Emaciated and half demented, he no longer knew anything except that he was instinctively cling-ing to the raft. When he was delirious and beyond hope he realized that strangers were nearby and that his raft was being pulled to shore. He learned that this was the Mormon town of Callville, more than a hundred miles downstream from Grand Canyon, and that he was saved.

It took James White a full week to recover from his ordeal and the men at Callville took care of him. He told them his story in detail, as well as he could remember it, and they took it for granted that he must have come on a raft through the canyons of the Colorado River. Since White never knew where he was at any time during his adventures he could not say exactly where he had been. But the men at Callville could tell him. Nobody had ever come through the long chain of canyons before, but now White had proved that it could be done. He had been the first man to complete a journey down the Colorado River.

This fact meant nothing to White, but, as he recuperated, he saw that his hosts were immeasurably impressed with his exploit. It was told and retold and the details became more vivid and dramatic with each telling. White, however, stuck to his original story; it was strong enough without further embellishments. Being without funds or friends, except the men at Callville, White remained at this small settlement at the head of navigation on the Colorado, and when he had entirely recovered he went to work for his benefactor, James Ferry. News of his remarkable exploit spread from Callville to San Francisco.

E. B. Grandin wrote a letter to the daily *Alta California*, and on September 24, 1867, this paper published Grandin's letter telling of White's adventure. Grandin placed the start of White's river journey at the confluence of the Green River with the Colorado River in Utah—a journey of some five hundred and fifty miles! And he took it for granted that White came through in fourteen days. As nobody knew anything about the intervening country and canyons, this was accepted by all, including White himself. They told him that that was where he started so he got that fixed in his mind. No matter how his story varied, he always insisted that he began his river journey that far upstream.

The story continued to spread. Dr. C. C. Parry, who was attached to a party making railroad surveys in 1867, heard the story at Hardyville, farther down the river, and wrote an account of it to General William J. Palmer who was chief of the survey. Dr. Parry accepted the White story in itself, which is just, but unfortunately he also accepted the interpretations as to distance which were so erroneously assumed at Callville.

The total facts in the case were that James White arrived in a dying condition at Callville, having come from some distance upstream though nobody could say just how far.

Callville's amazement and enthusiasm made it a five-hundred-and-fifty-mile trip.

Some months later, Dr. Parry accepted this and based a report on it which he regarded as more accurate than that of Lieutenant Ives and J. S. Newberry, although at the time he had not talked to White. Later he did meet White, and made notes from White's remarks, but by this time White himself had become convinced that he had passed through the canyons of the Colorado and he told Parry he had come all the way from the Green River in Utah.

Parry passed this information on to General Palmer who accepted it since Parry had got it from White himself.

Thus the legend grew. At first there were a few men and finally a dozen and then twenty and then many more who said James White was the first man through the Grand Canyon.

In 1869 Major Powell made his first trip and there was no doubt about where he started, where he went, and where he finished. He went from Wyoming to Callville and when he got to the latter place he heard the White legend. He said that it was obviously impossible, that no raft could last through the three hundred bad rapids, that no man alone could survive, and that it would take not fourteen days but six weeks at the least to run from the Green River to Callville. He knew; he had just done it. And he summed it up by calling White a "monumental prevaricator," and just in case that was not clear, once and for all, he rephrased it in simpler English and called White "the biggest liar that ever told a tale about the Colorado River." With that, the Major closed the door on the White legend and never deigned to mention it in any of his writings.

But slamming the door in the face of the legend was not enough. White's advocates rushed to the rescue. Their man, they pointed out, was prospecting near the confluence of the Green and the Colorado. He was chased by Indians; he built a raft; and he came out at Callville five hundred and more miles downstream. Let Major Powell, or anybody else, explain that if they could.

Still the pro-White faction was denounced by every man who ever went down the river from the Major on up to Emery and Ellsworth Kolb. One after another, those who ran the river and lived to tell it, repudiated White. No matter what he said or what proof existed, it simply could not be done and White never did it.

It settled down to a bickering of "he did—he didn't; he did—he didn't." And in the heat of the argument everybody forgot to ask White. When they looked for him he had disappeared. The greatest Colorado River controversy remained unsolved.

But the correct answer lay somewhere. Some logical and satisfactory explanation for all parties concerned had to be found. And it remained for the orderly and painstaking mind of Robert Brewster Stanton to find it. Stanton, it will be remembered, was second in command of the tragic Brown-Stanton party who went through the Grand Canyon and the adjacent canyons in 1889 to survey for a railroad. Though it all came to nothing, Stanton's interest in the river and the canyons never flagged. He wrote a long and meticulous manuscript presenting an engineer's point of view on every aspect of the area. And he included the long-argued White controversy.

After White appeared at Callville in 1867, the "he did—

he didn't" issue lasted for forty years. In 1907 Stanton found James White, who was then seventy years old, in Trinidad, Colorado, and he called on him and they had a long interview. From this discussion Stanton solved the riddle to his own satisfaction, but his solution did not satisfy the pro-White faction. The fight went on for another ten years. And in 1917, when White was eighty, the battle reached Washington and a round was fought in the United States Senate. The White faction won the round; the United States Senate in 1917 accepted the evidence that James White was the first man to pass through the Grand Canyon of the Colorado. Thomas F. Dawson and Senator Shafroth of Colorado carried the banner for White and apparently they settled the long quarrel in White's favor once and for all. And the anti-White supporters, especially Major Powell, Frederick S. Dellenbaugh, Robert Brewster Stanton, and the Kolb Brothers, were severely rebuked in Thomas Dawson's report and pamphlet printed by the Government Printing Office in Washington. There was much talk of removing the Powell monument at Grand Canyon and replacing it with one to James White.

But Stanton would not be licked. The same spirit that enabled him finally to run the Colorado from the canyon regions to tidewater, prevented him from surrendering in 1917. He collected all his evidence; he culled those parts from his unprinted manuscript that bore upon the issue; and he set to work to bring the true facts to the public. It was a labor of love on the part of a mind devoted to the truth, the plain truth, the whole truth, and nothing but the truth. The fight went on until 1922 and Stanton was unable to get his work published. In that year, at the age of seventy-six, he died. Still living was Frederick S. Dellenbaugh, of the second Powell expedition, who had also written to prove that the White story was a fallacy. But Dellenbaugh, too, was in his declining years. There seemed to be none of the older generation of Colorado River heroes left to carry on the fight.

But Stanton's manuscript came into the hands of James M. Chalfant who proceeded to carry on with Stanton's zeal. And in 1932 Chalfant edited Stanton's work called *Colorado River Controversies* and it was at last published in New York.

It was just sixty-five years since the controversy had begun, and most of the participants were dead. But the issue was nonetheless hot. Stanton's book concludes the argument. It leaves no room for doubt. It answers every question. It is final. James White did *not* pass through the Grand Canyon at any time in his life and Major Powell's monument stands.

But what James White did and where he went and how he got to Callville by raft, these, together with Stanton's infinite patience in setting the whole story to rights, are another chapter. It concludes a Colorado River and Grand Canyon epoch. It rings down a curtain; if it were not for Stanton, the farce or tragedy might be going on yet, and that would be too bad. For this long argument and the human bickering that went with it, not to mention the time and money wasted in proving for posterity that on the one hand it was Tweedledum and on the other it was Tweedledee, bring to a close a pioneering chapter in the history of the Grand Canyon. It can never happen again and now the truth can be told.

Tweedledum and Tweedledee

THE long fight over who first passed through the Grand Canyon is not the only argument that has come out of the great chasm. Men have quarreled over many other points and one is the question of why the three members of the first Powell expedition quit at Separation Rapids and went out of the canyon overland instead of seeing the voyage through to the finish. Some say this desertion was not caused by fear of the rapids, but was ordered by Major Powell himself, and that tension between the members and Powell had reached a breaking point. Some say that Powell and the two Howland brothers and Dunn had fought continuously and that Powell called the Dirty Devil River by that name simply because he said it reminded him of Dunn who was a dirty devil on all accounts.

If such bellicose conditions existed, Powell very properly kept them out of his records. There was no place for calumny in his reports to Washington. The Major may have made mistakes, but the purpose of his trip was to present a scientific report and he was not interested in vilification. Attempts have been made to reopen the case and expose the human problems and tangles, but most of these have been unsuccessful. It may be safely said that Major Powell was too big a man to dwell upon the human frailties. The canyon was his interest and no petty personal problems were worth consideration. History and science have approved the policy of the Major.

But the case of James White could not be so forthrightly dismissed. If he traveled through the length of the Grand Canyon in 1867, history wanted to know it and pay him proper homage. If he had not made this journey, history wanted to know it and put White in the niche he deserved. The whole discussion depended upon White who did not know what he had done or where he had been at any time, and thus the protagonist was an impossible witness either for or against himself.

A number of factors in the case, however, helped point to the truth. The first and most important of these was a letter that White wrote to his brother in Wisconsin eighteen days after he had been pulled off his raft at Callville.

This letter was the only honest account in print and was written when the events were fresh in White's mind, although much of what he went through was a confused phantasmagoria of impressions, and actual figures such as number of days, and time of day, cannot be relied upon at all.

The letter was published (after proper editing and correction of grammar and spelling) by a Colorado newspaper, the *Rocky Mountain News*, in February, 1869. It was printed again, with photographic reproduction, in *Outing* magazine for April, 1907. It was printed a third time in 1920, in a pamphlet by William Wallace Bass, a well-known character and long-time resident of the South Rim, who accepted the story and was strong in his support of White. And it was printed for a fourth time in Robert Brewster Stanton's final analysis, *Colorado River Controversies*, in 1932.

Since the letter is unquestionably first-hand and authentic, and since it offers such an intimate introduction to James White himself, it is reproduced here as accurately as his peculiar style of composition can be approximated in print.

Callville September 26. 1867

Dear Brother it has ben some time senCe i have heard frome you i got no anCe from the last letter that i roat to you for i left soon after i rote i Went prospeCted with Captin Baker and gorge strole in the San Won montin Wee found vry god prospeCk but noth that wold pay then Wee stare down the San Won river wee travel down about 200 miles then Wee Cross over on Coloreado and Camp We lad over one day We found out that Wee Cold not travel down the river and our horse Wass Sore fite and Wee had may up our mines to turene baCk When Wei Was attaCked by 15 or 20 utes indis they Kill Baker and gorge strole and my self tok fore ropes off from our hourse and a ax ten pounds of flour and our gunns Wee had 15 millse to woak to Calarado Wee got to the river Jest at night Wee bilt a raft that night Wee had good sailing fro three days and the Fore day gorge strole was wash off the raft and down that left me alone i thought that it Wold be my time next i then pool off my boos and pands i then tide a rope to my wase I wend over falls from 10 to 15 feet hie my raft Wold tip over three and fore times a day the thurd day Wee loss our flour flour and fore seven days i had noth to eat to ralhhide nife Caber the 8. 9 days i got some musKit beens the 13 days a party of indis frendey they Wold not give me noth eat so I give my pistols for hine pards of a dog i ead one of for super and the other breakfast the 14 days i rive at Callville Whare i Was tak Care of by James ferry i was ten days With out pants or boos or hat i Was soon bornt so i Cold hadly Wolk the ingris tok 7 head horse from us Joosh i Can rite yu thalfe i under Went i see the hardes time that eny man ever did in the World but thatk god that i got thught saft i am Well a gin and i hope the few lines Will fine you all Well i sned my beCk respeCk to all Josh anCe this When you git it

DreCk you letter to

Callville, Arizona.
Josh ass Tom to anCy that letter i rote him sevel yeas a goe
James White

There are two important points in the letter. The first is his statement of traveling two hundred miles down the San Juan. From the place where they struck the San Juan it would not be possible to "travel down" the river for two hundred miles for it empties into the Colorado long before. The San Juan is canyon-locked most of its way to the Colorado and cannot be followed at all. What White meant was that they traveled in what he thought was the general direction of the San Juan. Two hundred miles of that would conceivably put them as far down as the Little Colorado somewhere near what is now Cameron today. In fact, it would take them a little farther, or onto the Coconino Plateau country near the South Rim of the Grand Canyon.

As White had as little conception of time as he had of geography, he was never able to say how long it took the three of them to cover these two hundred miles. But in checking his dates, Stanton discovered that the three traveled for at least three weeks. As they were capable of making an average of twenty-five miles a day, and allowing half the time for prospecting as they went, the party could have made two hundred and fifty to three hundred miles which is just about what they did. This would put them even farther west, or roughly around the head of Diamond Creek on or about the end of August, 1867.

Somewhere in this area the Indians killed Baker. White said they were Utes, but obviously they were not because Utes never roamed south of the Grand Canyon. White called them Utes because that was a name with which he had become familiar in Colorado. It is possible that a roving band of Apaches had discovered the three white men. The ambush attack is symptomatic of Apache technique, and often these central Arizona Indians came north to the canyon country to raid the Havasupais and the Walapais who lived in terror of them.

Down either Diamond Creek or Spencer Canyon, then, fled White and Strole. They reached the Colorado eighty or a hundred miles above Callville, and either at the western end of Grand Canyon or twenty miles below. The rest of White's trip to Callville is told best in his own words except that he probably was on the river from eight to ten days. This retracing of the journey accounts for his later remarks about canyon walls of yellowish limestone. Had he passed through the Grand Canyon he would have seen no limestone but plenty of dark igneous schist and granite instead and he knew enough about types of rock to be able to recognize them. Moreover, had he passed through the Grand Canyon or any part of it, he would have experienced dozens of bad rapids. Since White reported only one really bad rapid it must have been the last of the series of man-killers, the vicious Lava Cliff group. These rapids drowned George Strole and after that White's trouble was not rapids but exposure and starvation until he reached Callville. Thus he probably first saw the Colorado at Spencer Canyon rather than Diamond Creek or he would have reported two bad rapids—Separation as well as Lava Cliff.

All of this information was carefully extracted from White in 1907, forty years after it happened, by Stanton who had it taken down by a stenographer and sworn to by a notary. It completely knocks the props out from under the Senate acceptance of White's five-hundred-and-fifty-mile journey from the Green River in Utah to Callville. White traveled less than a hundred miles on the Colorado and never saw the Grand Canyon. White himself was not to blame for the legend that grew up around him. He was totally ignorant of all the extenuating circumstances and he only repeated what other men told him he had done. If they had told him he had started on the Mississippi, he would have taken their word for it. Stanton gave him twenty-five dollars to tell the truth in 1907 and he told in detail the same story that he wrote to his brother in 1867. But it was not until 1932 that Stanton's evidence was presented to the public.

So the year 1932 brought to a conclusion the pioneering and explorative period of Grand Canyon and Colorado River history. It wrote the last paragraph, punctuated it, and closed the book.

Both the river and the canyon had, as far as men were concerned, entered the second period which might be called the tourist era. There is no date-line of demarkation between the two, but the fact that the tourist period is now in its prime is proved by many bits of evidence. One is the Norman Nevills expeditions. In recent years Mr. Nevills has been through the Grand Canyon a number of times. He takes passengers, for a price, and if you wish to follow the trail of the pioneers, Mr. Nevills will be your guide. You will get wet and enjoy a few thrills but you will be comparatively safe and you will not even have to row your own boat unless you want to.

And as to further evidence there is an advertisement of one of Mr. Nevills' rivals in business which has appeared in the *Desert Magazine* which reads:

COLORADO RIVER

200 miles of the finest scenery outdoors. See Rainbow Arch, Gregory Bridge, Crossing of the Fathers, Hole-In-the-Rock, and other historic spots. Explore for cliff dwellings, petroglyphs, and early Spanish inscriptions. *No bad rapids*. Personally conducted, everything furnished. Two weeks on the river. . . .

Compare that with White, Powell, Brown-Stanton, and all the others. How times have changed! Nevertheless, the beast is still there. He will decide whether he is going to offer you bad rapids or not. Row your boat gently down the stream, and trust him at your peril.

IV

South Rim

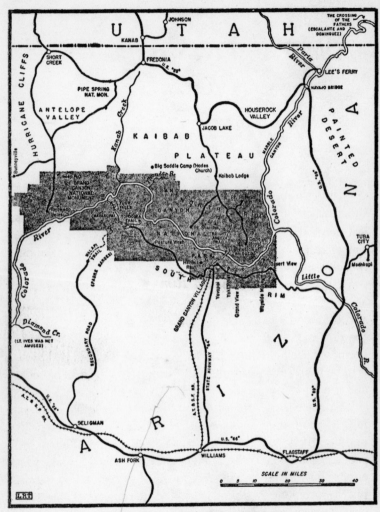

GRAND CANYON REGION

"Oh, Yes—I've Seen the Grand Canyon"

GREATNESS in any art is not necessarily simplicity; but great art invariably calls for a simple reaction. No matter how complex the subject, the audience-response should be pure and uninvolved.

Such statements are semantically dangerous as words such as "greatness" and "simplicity" are boundless, yet relative, and have no absolute meaning when used so glibly. To avoid the quicksands of meaningless verbiage it might be wiser to be more specific. Thus: the music of Beethoven and Varese is to be heard; the painting of El Greco and Klee is to be seen; and the art of the Grand Canyon is to be experienced.

The reactions of people to the Grand Canyon are interesting. Most of them are honest. They just give up. There is nothing to say; it is there and it is to be experienced. The impact on the consciousness when a visitor takes a look from either rim for the first time is stunning. Charles F. Lummis put it succinctly in these words: "I have seen people rave over it; better people struck dumb with it; even strong men who cried over it; but I have never yet seen the man or woman that expected it."

It is often the case that those who appreciate the Grand Canyon most make the mistake of trying to put it into words or paint. Their intentions are good; they want to pass their pleasure on for the enjoyment of others. Probably that can't be done. Paint won't do it and words won't do it; and as for the reams of poetry that have been written about it, they are best forgotten. Ferde Grofe made a bold and laudatory effort in music with his *Grand Canyon Suite*. The first time you hear it, it is good, but somehow it doesn't hold up. The best thing in it is the rather too obvious, little *morceau caractéristique* called *Down The Trail*. This is mule music, and the mule rhythm is amusing and accurate. If you go down the Bright Angel or the Kaibab Trails, your mule's jogging gait will recall the music to you at once. It is clever. But it might be about any mules anywhere. One might as well call *Pacific 231* Grand Canyon music because the Santa Fe engines come rolling up to the South Rim every day.

So it is not possible to transfer the greatness of the Grand Canyon to any other medium. The most successful attempt is probably in photography. Some excellent work has been done in this line, along with many failures. It takes a master technician with a camera. Give him a week and a good instrument and enough film or plates for a hundred pictures and his chances of getting two or three good ones are first-rate.

It will never do to discourage people from commenting on the Grand Canyon in whatever medium they choose. But that it unbalances most people's values—people of sensitivity and taste—is unfortunately true.

Try describing the Grand Canyon as an exercise in literary composition. The student who writes "The Grand Canyon is the Grand Canyon," period, and the one who turns in merely a blank sheet of paper, should win the highest grades.

Nevertheless, we all must try, and in this book I am leaving myself open to criticism time and again. Just as an example of what can happen, however, a few appreciative comments will illustrate the futility of words.

Charles F. Lummis wrote very well. His appreciation of the Southwest was deep and profound. His words, quoted above, are a fair sample. But overboard he went with this conglomeration: "Come—and penitent—ye of the United States, to marvel, upon this chiefest miracle of our own land."

He doesn't accomplish his end, I'm afraid, by an imperative, old English, and an archaic adjective.

And then there was John Muir who loved nature and wrote about nature and made fine observations. See what the Grand Canyon did to him:

"Wilderness so Godful, cosmic primeval, bestows a new sense of earth's beauty and size. But the colors, the living, rejoicing colors, chanting, morning and evening, in chorus to heaven."

Obviously he is trying to say something. But it is neither fact nor fancy, realism nor impressionism.

But the winner, to put a stop to Grand Canyon descriptions for a long time to come, is this:

"There is yellow—tawny, creamy golden yellow. There is orange—warm, glowing, gilded orange. There is white—frosted, silvery white. There is brown—hazel, fawn, cinnamon brown. There is red and scarlet and cardinal. There is vermilion and cerise, maroon and cherry. There is purple. There is blue. That is the Grand Canyon at mid-day, when the sun flattens the peaks and destroys the shadows.

"But look!—that vermilion now is russet, that cerise has turned to bronze, that maroon to copper, that cherry to sorrel, that yellow to dull gold. That whiteness now is ashen gray. That orange is brass, burnt, tarnished. That plateau is cast in copper. That gorge is set in iron. Those buttes are red, the temples are capped with red, even the air within is red!

"All other things failing, the Grand Canyon is red."

If I were to tell you the name of the author of that spectral binge you'd be surprised. A curtain of anonymity is charitable.

If description will never do, there is only one piece of advice left for those who are interested in the Grand Canyon: go see it for yourself.

It is not difficult to get there. The South Rim, open all year, is only sixty miles north from Williams, Arizona, which is on the main transcontinental line of the Santa Fe Railroad and U. S. Highway 66. Train service is daily and highways are excellent. Also one or two transcontinental flights send airplanes over it. You may also reach the canyon by driving north from Flagstaff, Arizona, and entering the park by way of the Navahopi Highway. Then you can leave by way of Williams. For westbound traffic this prevents duplication of route and is a highly spectacular approach. Do it in reverse if you're going east. Once you are there you will find accommodations at Grand Canyon village of all kinds for all pocketbooks.

If you want to go to the North Rim you must drive as there is no rail service. And you must do it between June first and October first because heavy snows close the roads in winter. The Union Pacific has a supplementary bus system which is first-class. You leave your train at the little town of Lund, Utah, and your bus detour may, if you wish, include Zion and Bryce National Parks, along with Cedar Breaks National Monument, and the Grand Canyon's North Rim. Accommodations, again, are of all kinds. If you come in your own car you may bring your camping equipment, or you may live in the sumptuous Grand Canyon Lodge on Bright Angel Point.

Occasionally the merits of the two rims are debated. The truth is that they are so totally different that there is little comparison. See them both. If not at the same time, then come back another time.

If put in a corner and asked, "I can only visit one rim, which shall I choose?" I believe I'd say, "See the South Rim first." Not that there is anything to choose from, and if I were going back right now for a month, I'd pick the North Rim. This is only because I have visited the North Rim fewer times than I have the South. I think the stranger gets a better and quicker understanding of the Grand Canyon at the South Rim. And it is more accessible. The North Rim is a postgraduate course; you'll want to take it; but don't begin beyond your depth. But again the choice is personal and again the answer is "Go and see for yourself."

Another question the stranger wants to know is "How long shall I stay?" Stay as long as you can. Stay an hour or a day or a week or a year. A lifetime won't begin to exhaust the place. One peek over the rim is better than not going at all. A day is better than a peek—and so on.

Sometimes visitors come in the morning, stay for a few hours, and leave in the afternoon. These are the people who say confidently, "Oh, yes—I've seen the Grand Canyon." They've seen something. Probably they'll never forget it. But they've not really experienced the Grand Canyon. Ask Emery Kolb; he's been there since 1901; he hasn't seen it all yet

In recent years the canyon has averaged more than a quarter of a million visitors annually. The rate will doubtless increase.

The first white men arrived in 1540, but the first brown-skinned man arrived long before that. The rims of the canyon seem a barren and hostile place for gregarious-minded man, but oddly enough this area was first visited, and even inhabited, by a dark-skinned race long before there was a European civilization. The date that the first pair of human eyes looked into the great gorge can never be established. But anthropology and ethnology prove that the Grand Canyon has been receiving visitors for at least sixty thousand years.

A race which science calls the Proto-Australoid migrated from southern and central Asia, perhaps forcibly driven by the Mongoloid stock, and crossed the land bridge from Asia to North America by way of the Bering Straits. This was about eighty thousand years ago. They were primitive men but they had developed the power of speech and the idea of taboo. As the migratory waves washed over the continent, these people became some of the first families of Arizona. One of their number is doubtless the first unsung discoverer of the Grand Canyon. When you stand on the South Rim and watch the play of the light and the changing forms and colors, remember that a long-headed, short-statured, brown-skinned man did the same thing sixty thousand or more years ago.

Those Who Came Before

ARIZONA has had four distinct cultures. The first was the Hohokam. Since these people (the name is of recent Indian extraction and means "the ancient ones") lived mostly in southern Arizona they had little or no contact with the Grand Canyon, though it is highly probable that one of their kind may have been the canyon's first visitor.

If, however, the Hohokam did not reach the canyon area of Kaibab and Coconino country, then, without doubt, the first people on the scene were those of the Proto-Australoid migration, who are called, locally, and pedagogically, the Basketmakers. And even if the Hohokam were there first, they did not remain, and the Basketmakers were the first to make a habitat of the North and South Rims. These Basketmakers were the long-headed type, and they are known anthropologically as dolichocephalic. That sounds very impressive, but it simply means that their heads were longer in proportion to their width than those of later races, and that due to this elongation the cranial content of these people was not as great as that of those who followed them.

The name Basketmaker is pleasant-sounding and only partially accurate. They made a crude kind of basket, of course, but the greatest baskets of all time were not produced by them. The name has been given them because one of their obsequies consisted in placing a basket upside down over the face of a dead person.

About seventy thousand years ago there was a migration route between Asia and Alaska. In time this disappeared until today the distance between the continental tips is fifty-five miles at the Diomede Islands. But even now a crossing can be made on foot, it is said, when the intervening water is frozen solid, if you don't mind a fifty-five mile walk over ice. The Proto-Australoid people, however, had a land bridge, and followed the waterways into Canada, and on by way of the Great Slave and Great Bear Lakes and southward until they reached the Mississippi Valley. Here they fanned westward through Oklahoma and Texas to the American Southwest. Others of their kind moved on down the east coast of Mexico to Yucatan, Central, and South America. A lesser route is suggested down the Pacific Coast all the way from Alaska to Panama but was held pretty close to the seacoast by high mountains. The people of this age had contact with animals of the Pleistocene period such as the mastodon, the mammoth, the ground sloth, and the camel. It was a North America difficult for us to visualize today.

The migration route was closed about fifty thousand years ago, but again became practical about forty thousand years ago. This opening and closing of nature's "immigration law" occurred again about twenty thousand years ago. Thus there were three distinct waves of human beings appearing on the North American continent. And perhaps, apart from the general waves, there were smaller isolated groups coming in from time to time. The people of the latter waves were Mongoloid, Caspian, and Palae-Alpine races who moved on to Mexico and became the Mayans, the Toltecs, and the Aztecs.

For the long period of time extending from about seventy thousand years ago up to five hundred B.C., there is little evidence beyond artifacts to give an intimate picture of the inhabitants of continental United States, although there is no doubt that the Proto-Australoid stock evolved into such Indian tribes as the Iroquois and the Algonkins.

In the Southwest, the first of the Basketmakers stalked animals, lived in caves, and left very little in the line of evidence. These were called the Hunters and they reached their peak about 200 B.C. Without doubt they used the cliffs and caves of the Grand Canyon region.

The race grew a little more intelligent as the centuries rolled on, and the second period is that of the Farmers. Like their predecessors, they were little brown men, but less nomadic. They had corn, which perhaps came up from the more advanced Caspian, Mongoloid, and Palae-Alpine stock in Mexico, and they made brush shelters for storing food and in these they also buried their dead. Their outstanding achievement, however, was the *atlatl*, or spear-thrower. This was a primitive means of hurling a dart or spear at great speed over a considerable distance. It brought down animals and was the Basketmaker's greatest invention. This was the most advanced life in Arizona between the years A.D. 1 and A.D. 400. From A.D. 400 up to 700, the third Basketmaker period flourished—that of the Potter. These people discovered that sand or pulverized rock, if baked with the clay, would hold together. Since pottery making has long been one of the aboriginal arts of the Southwest it is interesting to see how it began. These people also used a pit-house, lived in small groups or villages, grew corn, squash, and beans, and were just beginning to perfect the bow and arrow when something happened. And it meant the end of the Basketmakers.

But nobody knows just what it was.

There are numerous theories and at times they assume the aspect of the argument about the Tonto Sea. In general, it was assumed that a new race came into the Southwest and either killed the Basketmakers, or drove them out, or absorbed them.

This new race marks the third of the Arizona cultures, and is called the Pueblo, and they are subdivided by ethnologists into five distinct and progressive units. They were more intelligent, improved the farming techniques, made better pottery, and lived in groups as self-sustaining economic units. They had short stocky bodies, but they did not have the dolichocephalic head. Instead, their heads were round with a larger cranial content—the Brachycephalic—and they spelled doom to their simpler predecessors.

Another and more recent theory holds that these people were actually of the same stock as the Basketmakers but that the shape of the head was altered due to the use of a cradleboard. Babies, fastened onto a hard-backed board, grew round-headed instead of long-headed. Thus it would be not ethnology, but fashion, that made the Basketmakers disappear. The argument is heated. Most anthropologists adhere to the former theory, and a growing number of archaeologists is accepting the latter. The choice is yours.

The round-headed Pueblo stock continued to thrive in the Southwest. The bow and arrow replaced the *atlatl*. Turkeys were domesticated (only the dog had been previously tamed) and the people built the pueblos for which they are named. These small city-states evolved and their architecture and inhabitants may be seen today at Taos, Tesuque, Zuni, Walpi, Oraibi, Hotevilla, and numerous other places. In the Grand Canyon region there is evidence of the Basketmakers and considerable evidence of the Pueblo people. And while the flower of Pueblo civilization, which reached its peak between 1100 and 1300, was farther east in Arizona and New Mexico, the Grand Canyon area was well populated. Over three hundred pueblo ruins have been found within the national park boundaries. Many of these are small, some are in caves or overhanging ledges of rock, some are only food caches, and the majority are on the flat top of both rims. There is one large pueblo cliff dwelling on the North Rim at the base of the Coconino sandstone on the saddle of the Powell Mesa. It was two stories high and was inhabited from about the year 1000 to 1100 according to the opinion of Louis Schellbach, the present ranger-naturalist. There is another good example at Clear Creek. But both the Powell saddle and Clear Creek are difficult to reach and are seldom seen by the tourist. Within a few minutes' walk of Grand Canyon lodge on the North Rim, however, is an old cliff dwelling which is in a good state of preservation. You will probably be glad to take anyone's word for it, as to see it you must descend the face of the Kaibab limestone hand over hand on a rope.

The most accessible evidence of those who came before the white man is at the Wayside Museum on the South Rim about twenty miles east of Grand Canyon village. Here is an archaeological display with an archaeologist on hand to explain it to you. The place is called Tusayan which was not the name given to it by its original inhabitants. Tusayan was a name used by the Spaniards denoting the Hopi Indian country. For the want of a better name the scientists have called this pueblo by the name of the province—so Tusayan it is today.

It was built in 1185. It was two stories high with living rooms, storerooms, and an underground kiva, or ceremonial chamber. Underground is not quite accurate in this instance. Most kivas are beneath the earth, but in the case of Tusayan, the ground was so hard and the limestone so resistant, that the Tusayaners were content with a partially sunken ceremonial room and they let it go at that.

Nowhere in the building were there any doors. Entrance was by ladders and holes in the roof. This is typical of many pueblos and the purpose was to foil any marauders or raiders. By 1185 the Athapascan race had moved down from the north. These were the Navajos and the Apaches. They were nomads, fighters, killers. The Pueblo people were afraid of these American counterparts of the Goths and Visigoths, and their defense was their city without doors or even a breach in the walls. The system goes back to Troy and even earlier. The turtle perfected it first. It is all right if you are not starved out. It worked in the Middle Ages both in Europe and at the Grand Canyon, but it is only good as long as the defensive weapons—sheer walls—are stronger than the attacking power.

It is fitting that a professor of the University of Arizona should have developed a science which enables its scholars to determine with accuracy the age of pueblos such as Tusayan. It is very easy to write with assurance, "It was built in 1185," as I have done, but that statement would not be forthcoming without the meticulous research of Dr. A. E. Douglass, who developed the science of dendrochronology, or the study of the rings of trees.

Today everyone knows that the number of rings showing on the stump of a tree will tell you the exact age of the tree. If the tree was a hundred years old there will be a hundred rings, beginning with a dot or small circle at the center and counting out to the bark. When the rings are thin and ill defined the tree grew only slightly and thus it was a year of little rain. When the rings are broad it indicates that the tree was well nourished in those years and hence they were years of ample rain. This is dendrochronology in only its most broad strokes; the variations and ramifications are legion. But if you can establish a certain cross-section of log as being a hundred years old today, there will be definite characteristics of its early years which will show up as identical in logs which were old when the first tree was young. For example: suppose we are examining a log which we know is one hundred years old because we have just felled the tree and counted a hundred rings. And suppose the tenth ring has an unmistakable characteristic setting it apart as unique from all the others. And suppose that same characteristic occurs in another log, but occurs in its *one hundred and tenth* ring. Thus we know that both trees were growing in that same year, but that the second tree was one hundred years older than our first specimen.

By proceeding on this basis, the "bridge" method of tree rings, Dr. Douglass has, by extremely careful research, been able to trace back through time the climatic conditions of the Southwest as far as A.D. 11.

Moreover, as the science developed, it became possible to identify the age of logs by matching their rings to the established scale. Under a microscope tree rings are like fingerprints; each ring has its distinctive characteristics, and can therefore be identified with regard to those which precede and follow it. It is, therefore, quite possible to examine a cross-section of timber from a pueblo and say with authority: "This timber was cut in the year 1066—or 1492 or 517 or 1620." And this will tell you, almost to the year, when the pueblo was built.

Dendrochronology is no science for the amateur to pick up in an off moment, but its authenticity is beyond question. It has proven a great liaison-science to astronomy, archaeology, ethnology, ecology, and on down the line. Dr. Douglass has been at it since 1904 and his work has been of inestimable value in shedding light on the history of the Southwest. The science is young and its greatest contributions will conceivably be in the future. But if you want to know when the round-headed Pueblo people built Tusayan, Dr. Douglass can tell you to the year. The tree-rings of the timbers that were used prove that the trees from which the timbers came were felled in the year A.D. 1185. Admirable, remarkable, and thrilling, isn't it? Dr. Douglass and the University of Arizona deserve more than mere applause.

And now let us get back to the pueblo itself and the people who lived in it, people who could never have made a guess as to how keenly modern science would be able to read their history.

The site of Tusayan was not wisely selected, and why it was ever built is a bit of a mystery. There is no water near by, the land is unproductive, and certainly the Tusayaners were not interested in the view. Possibly it was used as a summer community only, as the winters on the South Rim can be severe. In order to get water the residents built a series of check dams, an ingenious method but not a guarantee that drought wouldn't dry up the small amount of water thus conserved. Only about thirty or forty people ever lived at Tusayan, and as there is no burial ground adjacent, it is probable that the building was not occupied for more than one generation. The absence of broken pottery in any quantity also substantiates this theory.

A great deal of work was done on it, however, and it must have proved a disappointment as a village because it was abandoned fairly early in the thirteenth century, possibly about the year 1230. The difficulties in maintaining a residence, coupled with attacks by Navajos proved too much for Tusayan. Once abandoned it was forgotten until 1930, some seven hundred years later, when archaeologists excavated the ruins, codified and classified the artifacts, built the present museum, and reconstructed the original community in a model done to scale. You may walk through the ruins today, and with a long stretch of the imagination you can recapture the life of seven hundred or more years ago. The canyon and the rim and the forest look just the same.

Many tourists stop at the Wayside Museum during the

summer months, and they, often without knowing it, represent the fourth of the Arizona cultures. First came the Hohokam, then the Basketmakers, then the Pueblos, and finally—as Hopi Indian wit has very accurately put it—came the Moneymakers.

And Those Who Came Later

B<small>Y</small> "MONEYMAKERS" the Hopis mean, of course, the wealthy tourists. Actually they are the money *spenders* who make the rim resorts possible and support the Hopi and Navajo Indian crafts by their purchases at Hopi House on the South Rim.

Those who really wanted to become the moneymakers at the Grand Canyon came before the tourists, and some of these have stayed on. After the aborigines came the soldier, the priest, and the scientist; but between this latter group and the contemporary tourist there was another group which did not fit into any of the above categories. They were all manner of men and might be called the Utilitarians or the Pragmatists since they came to make a practical thing of the canyon: miners, ranchers, hermits, free-lance explorers, nature-lovers, professional liars, and William Randolph Hearst.

One of the first of these to arrive was John Hance, sometimes known as Captain John Hance, but he was captain not of a company or a ship; he was instead a captain of mendacity. Hance is supposed to have arrived at the South Rim about 1881. Nobody could say where he came from or just what his previous profession had been. In those days of the West, it was not good taste to inquire too specifically into a man's past. It was a vital country; only the present mattered. If questioned, Hance replied, "I do not like ancient history." But he said it with a smile and he was a warm outgoing man and apparently everyone who knew him liked him.

John Hance loved the Grand Canyon. Its mysticism touched him and once that happened he was destined to live on the rim and in the bottom for the remainder of his life. It was a shrine and he had come to it; it was a sanctuary and he devoted himself to it; it was his pet and he liked to have it perform for strangers while he told tall tales about it. Hance was not a religious man. One of his friends once said, "Oh, he believed in God—I guess. But he believed mostly in the canyon and John Hance." If he had been told that the canyon had appealed to his latent sense of teleological inquiry he would have been nonplused and would have countered with some remark intended to astound his visitor and put him on the defensive.

His excuse for living on the South Rim was a mine. It was an asbestos mine deep down in the bottom where the second geological era had fused and pressed its elementary constituents some billion years ago until it had created this heat-resistant mineral. Asbestos mines are not common. Hance thought that he had a good thing, and he had. But like most other mineralogical efforts to make the Grand Canyon pay dividends, it failed because the cost of getting the product out of the canyon was prohibitive. Hance came, in time, to understand that his mine was impractical. But he never quite gave it up. It remained his excuse for living at the South Rim, although the real reason was his love for the canyon itself.

The first few tourists began to arrive in the late eighteen eighties. They came by stagecoach from Flagstaff over rough roads and there were no accommodations at the South Rim once they arrived. Naturally, they met Hance as his camp offered the only place to spend the night. Some of the more intrepid tourists wanted to go down into the canyon, and the only way to do that was to be guided by John Hance who had built a trail down to his asbestos mine. So, inadvertently and accidentally, John Hance found himself forced into the tourist business.

It was a happy incident.

It was worth more to him than his mine. He became the unofficial receptionist, guide, host, and storyteller to his unexpected visitors. And for these offices he was well qualified.

The Hance cabin was just east of Grand View Point, or about eighteen miles east of the present Grand Canyon village. Hance lived on the rim in the summer, and when winter snows made survival too hazardous, he descended his trail and lived below for months in the warmer Lower-Sonoran life zone of the canyon's depths. Thus by going up and down his trail he could select his climate at will. Hance never had any great amount of money (except for one windfall of ten thousand dollars for a mining claim—and with this he went to San Francisco where he spent the money in ten days) and there were times when the food problem was difficult. All supplies had to come from Flagstaff and in the eighteen eighties that was two days away. So, while life was glorious, life was not easy, and there were times when Hance literally did not have enough to eat. The tourist business corrected that condition, and by 1892 other men, ostensibly miners but destined to be drawn into the tourist trade as was Hance, had settled along the South Rim.

One of these was Pete Berry and he built the first hotel at Grand View Point in 1892. It was made of native logs and was supplemented by tents and the little settlement was at the head of what Berry called the Grand View Trail. Berry's Trail, like Hance's was built by himself and led down to some mines. Hance had asbestos, Berry had copper, but the Grand Canyon had them both.

Like Hance, Berry became a "dude wrangler" and three years later the Grand Canyon Copper Company, which was made up of Pete Berry and Ralph and Miles Cameron, constructed a three-story building at Grand View Point and went in for the tourist business, as well as copper mining.

The history of the Grand Canyon Copper Company is worth a brief examination. Although it never became a great corporation, its life was an index to American business organization and the eventual concentrating of control in the hands of one tycoon. Pete Berry found copper. Then a group of Arizona men formed a company. The company functioned but needed more capital to develop the natural resources. The original Arizona organizers sold control of the company to a group of Eastern men. The Grand Canyon Copper Company was reincorporated in New England. The president became John H. Page and the general manager was Harold Smith, neither of whom had anything to do with the immediate scene at the South Rim or the mines in the bottom, and the Grand Canyon Copper Company found itself a Vermont corporation with all records in Montpelier, Vermont. When the company failed to operate at a profit the men in control were no longer interested in keeping it a going concern. It cost twelve thousand dollars a year to keep the Grand View Trail open so that ten mules a day could each carry two hundred pounds of ore from the mines to the rim. The price of copper collapsed in 1907, and it was not worth the expense of getting the ore out of the mines. The company had other assets, notably the Grand View Hotel, but the Eastern promoters were interested in mining and not tourists. Just when the corporate superstructure began to topple over on the little fellows underneath, notably Pete Berry who now worked for the company that his strike had brought into being, William Randolph Hearst appeared on the scene and bought the entire property—mines, trail, mules, hotel, equipment, fixtures, and whatever future prospects there might be. Hearst was now the Grand Canyon Copper Company personified in one individual. He had no intention of operating the mines; he saw the rich tourist trade that was bound to come to the South Rim. He was going to exploit the Grand Canyon. The pattern might have run on along this line until it became Grand Hearst Canyon, but fortunately Washington stepped in and the area, after a long struggle, was made a National Park.

With all these elements seething about him, John Hance and his hit-or-miss tourist camp was left out in the cold. His gift was lying, not promotion. So following Ben Franklin's advice that if you can't defeat your rival you'd better join hands with him, John Hance became a fixture around the Grand View Hotel. For the next twenty-five years, he was a kind of privileged guest of the South Rim resorts. He had no official position but he was a "character" to the strangers and he entertained them with his adventures which he fabricated as he went along. He graduated to a kind of court fool or canyon clown, and in later years the Fred Harvey Company gave him room and board so that he would always be present to interest and astound their guests. And of this Hance never wearied. His method was to answer questions tirelessly and to begin a perfectly plausible story and let it drift into the impossible and fantastic while still holding the listeners' credulity. Then, when the tale had stretched far beyond reason, he would let it snap into absurdity and the tourists either loved it and enjoyed the joke, or pointed him out as a madman. At least they never forgot him.

Children loved John Hance, and to them he always explained how the canyon came into being. "I dug it," he would say simply. This story worked well for years until one little four-year-old girl asked seriously, "And where did you put the dirt?" Hance had no ready answer; he never used the story again. But it bothered him the rest of his life, and when he was dying he whispered to his waiting friends, "Where do you suppose I could have put that dirt?"

One of Hance's favorite stories was the fog yarn. At rare times the canyon will be filled with clouds. Both rims will be clear, but the depths will be concealed by a sea of fog temporarily locked within the walls. Hance would then bring out his snowshoes and casually approach whatever tourists might be at the rim.

"Well," he'd say to himself, "she's just about right to cross." Inevitably somebody would ask him what he meant.

"Oh, don't you know? Strangers here, eh? Well, say, too bad I haven't got another pair of snowshoes or you could join me."

"What are you going to do?"

"Whenever she fogs up good and solid like this, I always put on my snowshoes and take a walk across to the North Rim."

The startled visitors looked aghast, but hesitated to call the bluff for Hance was busy strapping on his snowshoes. He'd test them gingerly and add, "Yep, just right," and before the bewildered audience he would walk to the rim, stick a foot into space, and say, "Ah, that's just fine!" Then he'd stroll along the rim and call back to his audience, "It's a lot shorter if I start from Yaki Point. You just keep watching and tonight when you see a fire over on the North Rim you'll know I made it." And off he would go, disappearing along the rim walk in the direction of Yaki Point.

The next day he would be "back."

"See my fire last night?" he'd ask.

Once in a while somebody would say yes, and Hance would merely nod matter-of-factly. But as the answer was usually in the negative, he would say, "Well, the danged fog rose and blotted it out for you. I couldn't see your lights over here either. You know that blasted fog pretty near fooled me? It was good and thick goin' over but when I come back it was so thin that I sagged with every step. Once I thought I was goin' to hit bottom. Just like walkin' on a featherbed only worse. Plumb wore myself out gettin' back. You want to try it some time. Stay around a while and I'll lend you my snowshoes next time she fogs good and solid."

Other men, more famous in Arizona history than John Hance, also belonged to this pre-tourist era. One was William Owen O'Neill, better known as Bucky O'Neill, who died with his boots on during the charge of Colonel Roosevelt's Rough Riders at San Juan Hill. O'Neill had a series of exciting adventures in Tombstone and Prescott during the formative period of the West and it was because of his efforts that the Grand Canyon was at last served by a railroad. To this day it remains the only National Park with that distinction.

O'Neill had copper interests on the Coconino Plateau near the South Rim. A railroad was built north from Williams to the Anita Mine. Later this road was taken over by the Santa Fe, regraded, and extended to the South Rim. No longer was the jolting stagecoach journey necessary, and visitors began to arrive in great numbers. The Fred Harvey Company, in conjunction with the Santa Fe, built the popular El Tovar Hotel in 1904 and it became famous the world over for its unique location and its sumptuous (for 1904) accommodations. It is still functioning and while the years have somewhat dimmed its luster, it is not at all eclipsed by the more modern Bright Angel Lodge.

After 1904 the commercial aspect of the Grand Canyon was pretty much in the control of the Santa Fe and Fred Harvey. And as is customary in the tradition of both these institutions, they did a fine job. The Park Service took over administrative reins in 1919 and the Grand Canyon is now under the supervision of the Department of the Interior.

People who resent the doctrine of socialism, often overlook the fact that a form of socialism has worked in the guise of the Park Service for years. All National Parks are natural phenomena socialized for the use and benefit of everybody. The Grand Canyon is run by the government and this socialization has prevented its belonging to any individual from Vasquez de Coronado to William Randolph Hearst. It belongs to you.

Perhaps the last of the "practical" ventures at Grand Canyon, and one that is not without irony, occurred as late as 1937. It was not a moneymaking scheme. In fact, it was costly. But if those who backed it were able to declare their expenditures in their income tax as legitimate deductions in the interest of the advancement of science, they may have put their money to legitimate use after all.

From the South Rim at Grand Canyon village, looking off to the northwest, there is a large flat-topped formation known as Shiva Temple. Once it is identified for you it is unmistakable. Thousands of years of erosion have contrived to isolate a large section of what was once a part of the Kaibab Plateau of the North Rim. It is 7,650 feet above sea level, contains a forested area of six square miles, and up to 1937, it had never been explored because of its presumably unscalable walls. Here was an area that had been cut off from the rest of the plateau country for thousands of years, perhaps as many as fifty thousand. A scientific expedition led by Dr. Harold E. Anthony of the American Museum of Natural History, determined to scale Shiva and set foot on a part of the globe where no man, and certainly no white man, had ever set foot before. Because of its fifty thousand years of isolation it was expected that the flat top of Shiva Temple would yield specimens of plant and animal life of a forgotten world. If the animals that lived on this lone mesa had been cut off from their fellow creatures for all those centuries, they might conceivably be evolutionary freaks. Here was a section where time might have stood still, or even evolved in some unexpected manner. Anything could have happened on Shiva.

News of the expedition got abroad. Apparently the project was being very well done. Nothing was overlooked, and supplies which could not be transported up the sheer walls were to be dropped by parachute from an airplane. In September, 1937, the ascent began. It was extremely difficult and dangerous. And it was a thrill indeed to the members of the party who finally made the neck-breaking climb when they clambered over the rim and stood—the first human beings—on a part of the earth that had never been trod before, six square miles of virgin soil which no man had ever seen, six square miles that had been as remote through the centuries as if they had been six square miles on the moon or Mars.

And then things began to happen.

One of the party found a pair of deer horns. They all looked at each other blankly. Those deer horns were new. They had been dropped within the last year. How had the deer got up to this place? Nobody could say. Had they been here for fifty thousand years? Most unlikely.

They explored a little farther.

The next find was truly startling. It was a small yellow oblong box made of cardboard and printed on it in red letters were the words, "Eastman Kodak—panchromatic."

The jig was up. And while the daring explorers waited for their parachute-dropped supplies they almost hesitated to look farther. And finally, down from the skies, floated their sealed tins of water and food. It all became a bit ridiculous; and as one of the party declared, they would not have been surprised to find, in this place where man had never set foot, a movie company on location. The expedition had one satisfaction, however. They proved the practicality of being supplied in inaccessible places by air. A carton of eggs, among other things, came down by parachute and not an egg was broken.

But the expedition, no matter how bad the dent put in its prestige, did explore and record a section of the Grand Canyon terrain which had never been formally explored before. And as far as the fifty-thousand-year inaccessibility of Shiva was concerned, that myth was destroyed forever. Animals of all kinds seemed to have no trouble in making yearly ascents and descents. There was no difference whatever between the species on the isolated Shiva and those of the Kaibab Plateau. This was not the conclusion that the party had hoped to reach, but in the interests of science they could arrive at no other.

The pre-exploration publicity which had been serious and sober became somewhat derisive when the party returned. This was not entirely fair. The expedition had set forth in good faith. They had no way to foretell that the deer roamed Shiva at will. And as for the person who tossed away that empty box of film when he reloaded his camera—well, you couldn't kill him for that. But who in the name of Shiva was he?

His identity has never been firmly established, but those who know the Grand Canyon and its permanent residents smile knowingly. Whoever went up there was a photographer; he was not a stranger to the area; and he was adept at canyon-climbing. Does that fit anybody we know? We can put two and two together and get four or twenty-two depending upon how we put them together. Now the news had been bruited about that Shiva was to be scientifically scaled. Any explorations of that nature would have been bound to interest one or both of two brothers who were photographers and who were not strangers to the area and who were adept at canyon-climbing. No names or inscriptions were found by the scientific party on Shiva, but they might well have been, and if they had, there are only two names that would be logical. They are Ellsworth Kolb and Emery Kolb. If you are still in doubt, why not ask one of the brothers the next time you visit the South Rim?

Trail-Wise and Trail-Weary

ON THE Santa Fe train northbound from Williams:

"Darling, wasn't it thrilling?"

"Yes, dearestest. Mother said it was the prettiest wedding she ever saw."

"You looked lovely in her dress."

"Poor mother—she said she cried because she was so happy."

"I thought your father had a glint in his eye, too—especially when I called him Dad for the first time."

"He loved it, dearestest, I just know he did. They were reliving their own wedding all over again. That's one reason why they wanted us to come to the Grand Canyon for our honeymoon."

"We're almost there, too."

"Tickets, please."

"Oh—ah—yes—ah, conductor, my—er—wife—and I are visiting the Grand Canyon for the first time. What would you suggest that—ah—well, what is there to do after we get there?"

"Go down the trail on a mule."

"And then what?"

"Come back up again."

"Darling, did you hear what he said?"

"Well, I should say I did! What a strange man."

"It might be sort of fun, darling."

"But dearestest, mother and father never did that."

"I understand the mules are very safe."

"I wouldn't touch one for the world."

"Not even one eensy-weensy pat if I asked you to?"

"Oh, of course, I'd do *anything* for *you,* dearestest."

If the time was 1920 or thereabouts, they went down the Bright Angel Trail. If it is today it is probable they used the newer Kaibab Trail. The Grand Canyon has long been a popular resort for honeymooners, and almost all of them take the muleback trip from rim to river. It is, without doubt, the most inopportune time to take such a trip, but if they survive it, and still love each other (as most of them do), the marriage is going to be a success.

Everybody who has ever visited the Grand Canyon is familiar with the famous Bright Angel Trail even if he has only stood at the rim and peered below to the halfway mark at Indian Gardens on the Tonto shelf. But most visitors do not discover that there are many trails in the park, some advisable and some inadvisable. On the South Rim there are eleven trails that lead from rim to river, and on the North Rim there are four, and while some of these are abandoned and dangerous, a few of them are in good condition and offer a variation on the tourist routine. If, however, you are visiting the canyon for the first time, or if you are bride and groom, by all means stick to the conventional and confine your explorations to one of the prepared trips.

The Bright Angel Trail begins at the full arc of the embayment created by the Bright Angel Fault. This giant earthquake crack runs almost north and south, diagonal to the general course of the canyon and the river. On the North Rim the erosion has followed this fissure and created the great Bright Angel Canyon. On the South Rim the head of the trail begins literally in Emery Kolb's backyard. Thus it is within easy walking distance of hotel, lodge, and camp ground, and one of the favorite sports of those who do not go down the trail is to gather at the starting point and watch the muleback parties take off. Many of these people have never been on a mule before, and as some of them insist upon acting as if the mule had never been previously ridden, it is sometimes a spectacle to watch. The dude takes it for granted that he is guiding his mule. Actually the mule has done this so many times, for so many years, that his intelligence and *savoir faire* far surpass that of his rider. The excited and loud-talking tenderfoot can pull up on the bit or relax, but the mule will go about his own business of navigating the Bright Angel Trail with no more concern than if he were carrying a sack of potatoes. The rider learns the animal's name and he likes to say, "Whoa, there, Yaki," or "Giddap, Nugget," and never comprehends that Yaki and Nugget are whoaing or giddapping of their own good judgment. Some mules are more nervous than others, some are definitely temperamental. All of them have a sense of humor and love to play. But a mule can be serious. He has his time for work and time for relaxation (watch them relax some time in the big Fred Harvey corral at the main stables—it's worth observing) and he never suffers from a duality of purpose. He works with careful intent; he plays with gay abandon. Going up or down the trail is work and his judgment is always good. No mule ever takes an unnecessary chance and no mule will become panicky unless he is deliberately abused or frightened.

Some timid tourists like to pet their animal's nose and try to get acquainted by giving him sugar or cake. He doesn't care for nose petting and will coldly turn the other way. He will always take the sugar or cake with indifference and ingratitude, and with a look in his calculating eye which says, "All right, if you want to feed me, sucker, I'll eat, but it's not getting *you* anything." You're still just a sack of potatoes to him.

The mules are creatures of habit. They have a routine that they like, such as walking or trotting at certain places, drinking at a specific point, and selecting a special place on the trail to urinate and doing so without fail every time they come to it. There is no doubt that a mule waits of his own accord until he arrives at his favorite spot. Then he casually stops, relieves himself, and goes on. Each mule in the party will do the same. It is mule decorum and you can't violate it.

Other characteristics of the mule are eating as he walks and scratching himself on certain favorite bushes. A succulent crop of grass or a mouthful of willow leaves, or even cottonwood leaves, are nice to chew on when you're hauling a sack of potatoes on your back which insists upon making idle remarks to you, calling to the people ahead or behind, and snapping pictures as you jog along. As to scratching, if you have had an annoying itch on your left flank all day long, and you remember a nice scratching that you had at a certain bush near the Devil's Corkscrew, you are naturally going to scratch yourself there again just as soon as you come to it. So you do, and the stout lady on your back calls, "Oh, guide—he's leaning way over the edge!" How can you be expected to explain that your favorite scratching bush is on the outside edge of the trail where an inch more means a five-hundred-foot drop. You aren't going to slip—you've scratched here a dozen times in the last month. But a sack of potatoes can't be expected to know that. You snort and jog on with just a little more jolt than usual. After all, even a sack of potatoes might get a headache, and wouldn't that be too bad.

On the Bright Angel the descent is quick. The trail switch-backs and zigzags down the face of the Kaibab limestone, the Coconino sandstone (a section of the trail is called "Jacob's Ladder"), the Supai formation, the Redwall, and levels off on the Bright Angel shale of the Tonto group at Indian Gardens. This is a small oasis that from the rim seems to be a patch of green and nothing more. It is the halfway mark for mule parties; rest, lunch, talk, and so on. From this point on, the trail follows Pipe Creek, the Devil's Corkscrew, and emerges through a side canyon to the inner gorge and the rushing, roaring, swirling Colorado River. And just as the conductor on the train said, the next event is to ride back up again. It is not an easy one-day trip for tourists who are not used to the saddle. But if the geological significance complements, for the visitor, his exposure to the stunning adjective-beggaring scenery, he will find the thrill worth any hardship between rim and river. It is a trip you can never forget, and long after the weariness from the experience has worn off with the help of a hot bath and a neat whiskey, the memory will remain. You may say, "Never again," but if you return to the park five years later, or ten years later, you will insist upon doing it again and you'll sell the idea to whoever may be with you. The Grand Canyon will always be incomplete for you without this experience. It doesn't matter which trail you use, but, some time, go from rim to river and back.

The Bright Angel Trail has a curious history. It was begun by animals and was doubtless a deer trail for centuries. Then it was used by the Havasupai Indians who went from the rim to the Tonto shelf to farm and make use of the spring at Indian Gardens. When this trail was first used by men it is not possible to say, but unquestionably it is one of the oldest trails in the area and may have been in existence in Basketmaker times. Promoter Ralph Cameron and Pete Berry made some improvements on the Indian efforts in 1890 and the trail became reasonably safe. Cameron had an eye on mining possibilities on the Tonto shelf and the trail was private property and remained so up until 1928. Cameron made more money from charging tolls on the Bright Angel than he did out of any mines in the canyon. After Cameron's title passed to the county, the tolls were continued, but in 1928, after a very complicated deal, the trail became the property of the National Park Service which, of course, it should have been long before. Today it is considered a boulevard by old-timers at the canyon. It is broad and safe with occasional water fountains and emergency telephones, and all its hazards lie in the minds of its inexperienced travelers.

Pipe Creek, incidentally, on the lower half of the trail was named by Ralph Cameron because of a joke. In 1894, four hardy men came along the Tonto shelf from Grand View Point to the Devil's Corkscrew area. Cameron led the way and was considerably ahead of his three companions. Working his way up the creek that leads to Indian Gardens he found an old Meerschaum pipe. He scratched a date on it and left it in such an obvious place on the trail that the three men following him could not miss it. But the date that Cameron scratched on it was 1794. Thus the pipe would seem to have been lost there just a hundred years before. Of course, the others found it and brought it along. In camp at Indian Gardens there was much speculation and argument as to who had been deep down in the Grand Canyon in 1794. Cameron saw that the story was going to be accepted and would gain momentum, so he very wisely exposed his hand and the joke. The men were more angry at the collapse of the yarn than they were satisfied over hearing the truth. But the stream was always referred to thereafter as Pipe Creek. Today the Bright Angel Trail follows Pipe Creek, and after you have rested at Indian Gardens and wondered how much farther it is to the river, you will descend for a mile or so along the creek named for Cameron's jest.

To the east of the Bright Angel on the South Rim there

are four (really five) trails that lead to the river. They are the Kaibab, the Grand View, the Hance, and the Tanner. This last includes an old mining trail known as the Bunker.

The Kaibab Trail is without doubt the finest in the canyon from a standpoint of engineering skill and comfort. And, for that matter, it takes no second place for scenery. It lacks the history and color of the Bright Angel. It is well graded and wide and banked, and somebody bet that he could ride a motorcycle down to the river and back. Rather fortunately the bet was never taken. It was built as late as 1928, entirely manmade, following no animal trails, and is the shortest route to the river and Phantom Ranch and Bright Angel Canyon on the north side. The Kaibab and the extended Bright Angel really merge just before the suspension bridge which is the only means of crossing the river.

Phantom Ranch lies near the mouth of Bright Angel Creek and this is a popular two-day trip; that is, the traveler goes down either the Bright Angel or the Kaibab and returns by the other after a night at the Ranch deep down in the fastness of the two billion-year-old Archean rocks where the first live thing met the second live thing those many years ago.

The Kaibab Trail continues on up the long Bright Angel Canyon on the north side and here there are such sights as Altar Falls on Ribbon Creek and Roaring Springs which come cascading out of the base of the great Red Wall. They are phenomena of the Grand Canyon that make beautiful and exciting side trips, and mule and outdoor enthusiasts won't want to miss them. The route of the Kaibab Trail from Phantom Ranch to the North Rim is fascinating scenically and of great importance to the student or scientist generally interested in geology, botany, and the flora and fauna in particular of the Upper and Lower Sonoran life zones as well as the Transition and the Canadian. You can't ride up and down these canyons, change altitude speedily, and move from desert country like that of Mexico to timber land like that of Canada in a few miles without having interesting things happen. But you must be equipped to understand what is going on around you in nature, or you will be more preoccupied with the hardness of your saddle than with anything else. And that would be too bad.

The improved Kaibab Trail forces your mule to ford the delightful Bright Angel Creek seven times between Phantom Ranch and the North Rim. The original trail in this section was made by Francois E. Matthes with a U. S. Geological Survey party in 1902. This party had to cross the creek ninety-four times in seven miles, a fact which helps you appreciate the improved Kaibab today.

Back on the South Rim, east from the Kaibab Trail, is the Grand View Trail. This is not in good condition today and is not recommended for amateurs in canyon-climbing. It was originally Pete Berry's trail to the mines of the Grand Canyon Copper Company and for experienced hikers it is a good individual trip. But, if you attempt it, you had better carry an alpine stock and some water and advise the Park Service of your exploit first.

A little farther east is the Hance Trail where the lying captain used to descend to the greatest asbestos mine in the world—which never produced very much asbestos. The trail followed an old Indian route which was a mere foothold along the canyon walls. It is not impossible that this may have been the trail down which went the "three lightest and most agile men" of Cardenas, the canyon's first white visitors in 1540. Certainly the Spaniards used an Indian trail for there were no others in those days. Whether this is true or not, the trail still has claims to historical fact for it was by this route that the first white woman ever penetrated the canyon. She was Mrs. Edward Ayers, the wife of a Flagstaff lumberman, and she reached the bottom of the canyon in February, 1882, for whatever that data may be worth. Certainly no white woman had ever been there before. Hance used to have a sign on his trail reading "Fifth Avenue" which was thought to be very funny; and he had another sign of more practical significance reading, "Toll on Trail: Foot Man $1.00, Saddle animals $2.00." This abrupt message now rests in the Park historical collection in Grand Canyon village. Since Hance had no legal claim to the trail at all except perhaps squatter's rights, it is quite in character that he should have charged admission to it.

The most eastern trail leading from South Rim to river begins at Desert View Point and is the Tanner Trail, though an earlier name was more picturesque, Horsethief Trail. This began as a deer run and became an Indian Trail, and was used in the eighteen sixties by the Navajo Indians who were then fleeing before the onslaughts of the man who was oddly both their enemy and friend, the Man Who Talked One Way, better known to most Americans as Kit Carson. A Navajo chief called Old Begonia led a number of his people down this trail to escape capture by the white soldiers.

In the summer of 1889, three prospectors, Tanner, Bedlias, and Bunker, improved the trail and added a new section near the rim which is sometimes called the Bunker Trail. Again the goal was copper and again the canyon made the hauling of the ore too difficult and too expensive.

The trail has continued to maintain its peculiar personality, however, as a retreat for escapists, criminals, and the socially misfit. For some odd reason there has always been shady activity of one kind or another associated with the Tanner Trail. One instance of this led to its being called Horsethief Trail, and at the time it was a hideout for renegades and poachers and other wanted men. For one reason, this was a remote section of the Grand Canyon country until the opening of the Navahopi Highway in 1935, and the law seldom penetrated into these wilds. The horsethieves had a good racket. They would steal animals from the Mormons in Utah, drive them down into Arizona and into the Nankoweap Basin on the north side of the Colorado River. This is reached by the Nankoweap Trail which offers plenty of rough going on the North Rim. Then the thieves had a ford at Chuar Creek which was very dangerous and passable only when the water was low. The stolen animals were then driven up the Tanner Trail and taken on to Flagstaff and sold. Then the thieves, well heeled, would steal another twenty or more head around Flagstaff and drive them back over the same route and sell them to the Mormons in Utah. There must have been a good profit in this shuttling of stock for it was referred to as the "Grand Canyon Horse and Mare Company" until some county sheriffs armed with shotguns finally discouraged further operations.

Throughout the eastern section of the Grand Canyon there are rock piles and cairns and claims indicating that this area was pretty well prospected. And during the years when Washington tried to enforce the Volstead Act the Tanner Trail again came into its own. Some person or persons unknown built a still in the region of Chuar Creek. It was the real thing and a good still and it turned out liquor while its operators scouted for "revenooers," and the raw whiskey was sent out over both Tanner and Nankoweap Trails. How much sour mash was fermented there will never be known unless the long-lost distillers will come forward. The remains of the still were found by ranger-naturalist Edwin D. McKee in 1933. Dr. McKee is now a professor of geology at the University of Arizona and, while he has never been interested in the whiskey business or the art of distilling, he knows where there is a first-class opening in a remarkably safe location if you are interested in taking a flier on your own.

Thus the renegade reputation of the Tanner Trail has come down through the years. And you may be sure that more will be heard of the Tanner in the future. It is too bad a boy to remain quiet. The trail itself is in poor condition today, but it can be traveled if you know where to look for it. Solo expeditions are discouraged, but if you are properly equipped and have the blessing of the Park Service the old Tanner may give you an exciting outing. And don't miss the still.

West from Grand Canyon village on the South Rim there are five trails all well known to residents of the area and little known to the average tourist. The first of these is the Hermit. It was built in 1911 by the Santa Fe for tourist use exclusively and to avoid paying the toll on the privately owned Bright Angel. There was an overnight resort at Hermit Camp which has been abandoned now that the more sumptuous Phantom Ranch is in operation. The Santa Fe and the Fred Harvey Company turned the trail over to the Park Service in 1919. It has gradually fallen into disuse although it is safe enough and can be traveled by anybody. Since the trail had no reason for existing beyond rivaling the Bright Angel, it lost even this excuse with the completion of the Kaibab. It extends from rim to river and offers an excellent trip. Many tourists used it between 1911 and 1919 and it is regrettable that this part of the Grand Canyon is losing out in tourist appeal. The name Hermit was given to it in honor of Louie Boucher who was the original hermit of Grand Canyon and who looked and acted the part. Unless the Park Service maintains the Hermit Trail it is slated for eventual oblivion along with the Grand View and the Hance.

A little farther west is the Boucher Trail which was the private trail of the hermit. He built it from 1889 to 1893 and it is an interesting trail indeed, entering Hermit Basin by way of Dripping Springs (springs seeping through overhanging ledges or caves). Deep down in the canyon lived Louie Boucher, and no questions asked please. Men usually have good reasons for becoming hermits and we shall respect those reasons, even though the Hermit of the Grand Canyon is no more. Louie was a typical desert rat of his day. He was a prospector and he was seldom seen without his pick and pan and tools. He owned several burros and a white mule of which he was very fond. He put a bell on the mule, and the tinkle could be heard for a great distance. It was an infallible sign of the approach of the Hermit with his prospector's trappings and his white beard and white mustache jogging along on his white mule. The Hermit lived in a white tent and "told only white lies" to white strangers. Herman Melville in his remarkable chapter on the history and significance of white in *Moby Dick* might have used with considerable effect the white predilections of Louie Boucher.

Quite some distance farther west, out of range of the average tourist, is the Bass Trail. It begins near Havasu Point and descends Bass Canyon, "crosses" the river (that is, W. W. Bass who built it had a boat and a crude cable crossing here at one time), and goes up Shinumo Creek on the north side. This trail is, in fact, known as the Shinumo Trail on the North Rim. W. W. Bass was a Grand Canyon character who was just as well known in his day as John Hance. But Bass was a serious fellow. Bass really studied the canyon. It is somewhat odd, however, that with his full knowledge of both canyon and river, Bass came to accept the James White myth of his trip from Utah to Callville on a raft. The palpable impossibility of the White yarn was so evident to canyon and rivermen that many of them didn't even take the trouble to scoff. Bass, however, wrote a pamphlet in 1920 defending James White and the fantastic story which we have discussed in full in another chapter.

The Bass Trail was originally built by the Havasupai Indians in order to get to Mystic Springs at the base of Mount Huethawali. An earthquake is supposed to have choked off the springs in the eighteen nineties, but this story has no authentication. At any rate, Bass improved the trail and was led to the springs by Captain Burro, a Havasupai Indian. Bass had located both copper and asbestos mines (going John Hance and Pete Berry one better) and the springs were of great value to him. He gave the Havasupai a sack of flour and half a beef and the Indian considered himself wealthy.

Again mining proved to be too difficult in the Grand Canyon but Bass loved the country and continued to develop it as best he could. As early as 1900 he put in his bid for the tourist trade. On the north side of the river, near the mouth of Shinumo Creek, Bass planted a fruit orchard and the place was known as Shinumo Gardens. It was the precursor of Phantom Ranch, which developed much the same way near the mouth of the Bright Angel Creek. Bass continued to live at the Grand Canyon through the years and died in 1933 at the age of eighty-four. Longevity goes with the canyon as long as you do not trifle too much with the river. As a tribute to Bass and the canyon trail he loved, his ashes were scattered over it by airplane.

Further west, so remote that it is out of the tourist category altogether, is the Great Thumb Trail. Even the number of park rangers who have seen this trail can be counted on the fingers of one hand. It was, or is, an Indian trail (the Havasupais again) and was used by them to descend from the rim to the red Tonto bench. It is said to be precarious indeed, and its purpose was to allow the Indian to hunt in a remote region. Very little more is known about it, and it is possible that it does not descend all the way to the river. Nobody could say for sure. Its chief interest lies in the fact that here, within thirty-five miles of civilization, is a trail leading into a canyon wilderness so difficult that it disappears into a labyrinthine limbo where nothing is known about it beyond supposition. Perhaps it has a Minotaur who devours those who follow it to its fateful end. If so it is today still awaiting its Theseus and

Ariadne. If you want adventure while you visit the Grand Canyon, explore the Great Thumb Trail. To the best of my knowledge it still remains to be done.

There is one more trail on the South Rim and that is the Topocoba. This can be reached over a road leading west from Grand Canyon village. It begins as a very good road. Some thirty-five miles later it is merely a rocky trail which comes to a precipitous end at Hilltop. Here the Topocoba begins. It descends Lee Canyon and finally enters Cataract Canyon and leads to Supai, the Havasupai Indian village in a place of great peace and beauty. We have had occasion to mention it previously as Father Garces in 1776, coming out of Havasupailand, climbed the Topocoba Trail. Lieutenant Ives missed it altogether in 1857, but Jacob Hamblin of the Mormons found it in the eighteen sixties. Since the trail belongs, properly, to a section on the Land of the Sky Blue Water, we need not dwell upon it here. It is possible to go all the way from Hilltop, via Supai, to the Colorado River at the mouth of Havasu Creek—possible, but highly improbable that the charm of Supai itself will permit you to carry out this intention if you have it. The Topocoba is in good condition, and while it is necessary to use Indian ponies instead of the reliable mule, the trail is scenically thrilling and historically exciting as you plod along, varying your gait perhaps with the restful lope so characteristic of the tough little Indian horse.

This brings us to the end of a survey that may leave us both trail-wise and trail-weary. But no second-hand description, no written words, can convey the adventures and pleasures to be found in exploring Grand Canyon trails. They come in all sizes, shapes, forms, and hazards from the tourist-guaranteed security of the Kaibab to the mysteries of the Great Thumb. You can do it by mule, horse, or on foot. And you will never be properly trail-wise nor grimly trail-weary until you try it for yourself.

One Hundred Million Customers

A VISITOR to whom mathematics was a religion was told at the South Rim that the Grand Canyon has been averaging a quarter of a million guests a year. He was also told that the first visitor arrived four hundred years ago. The worshiper of figures (and useless information) did some lightning calculating and came up with, "Four hundred times two hundred and fifty thousand is one hundred million. The place has had a hundred million customers! Wow! No wonder it's good!"

He then proceeded to figure out the average monetary expenditure of each individual visitor. Calculating that amount at a mean of ten dollars, he discovered that the Grand Canyon had earned one billion dollars gross since it had "been in business." He gasped, "Why, it's one of the biggest rackets in the country! I wish I owned a piece of it!"

The thing fascinated him and he used a large quantity of El Tovar stationery in embellishing his conclusions and piling up rich details, such as the amount of food consumed by guests and on down the line to the number of pairs of shoes that had been worn thin on the trails, the number of Ohs and Ahs that had been uttered at the rim, and the amount of profit that might have accrued to any one family had they kept this monopoly in their control for four generations. He hardly saw the canyon itself but he had an exhilarating night with figures and left the next morning perfectly satisfied with his visit, and secretly looking, no doubt, for a likely canyon in which to invest. If ever asked if he enjoyed the Grand Canyon, he unquestionably said, "I certainly did, you should go there. Why do you know that if one hundred million——" and so on.

Thus the Grand Canyon receives and accepts and sends away all types. It has all kinds of effects on all kinds of people, and perhaps it offers an index to its visitors' character. A barber who cut my hair at El Tovar had lived beside it for a number of years. He was against it. "That thing!" he said, resentfully. "I never look at it. Makes me nervous. But I guess some people like it. Aren't people funny? Straight back or part it?" The man really hated the canyon and he wasn't fooling. It was always there to annoy him and I shouldn't be surprised to read some day that he had gone berserk and jumped into it.

The statistics worshiper, incidentally, was absolutely correct in his mathematics, but his conclusions were wrong. The Grand Canyon has been averaging a quarter of a million guests per year only in recent years. The number is steadily growing and, just before World War II, the annual tourist total was up to about three hundred thousand. That's a lot of visitors. The canyon is still a long way from having its hundred millionth customer, but the day will come when he will arrive.

Who are these people?

Just about representative of every race, creed, and classification of mankind on earth. Probably there is nobody who can truthfully say, "No, I have no desire to see the Grand Canyon." Even a number of blind people have come to "see" it. A few years ago a blind man made the overnight trail trip down the Bright Angel to Phantom Ranch. He said he enjoyed it immensely and that he could sense the depth and that it became more and more exciting to him as the mule carried him deeper and deeper into the geological history of space, time, and the earth. He became a Grand Canyon enthusiast and probably got a lot more out of his experience than many people with sight.

A slightly different instance occurred on the North Rim. A woman who was going blind, an incurable case, wanted to see the colors of the aspen forest in the fall months. She regarded these trees as the most beautiful sight she had ever seen, and she wanted that to be the last image brought to her by her failing vision. And she carried this through so that her last visual recollection is the Kaibab Forest in October.

On the other hand, there was the New York executive who arrived with his secretary (male) and took a room overlooking the rim. His business of the day was incomplete and he began dictating immediately upon being installed in his room. The setting sun brought out the brilliant reds and yellows and contrasting colors and it bothered him as he paced between bed and dresser.

"Yours of the sixteenth instant in hand," he dictated. "Regarding same would say . . ." and he paced to the window and pulled down the shade to keep the glaring light out of his eyes. He completed his dictation at ten o'clock, had a late supper, and went to bed. He and the secretary left on the morning train immediately after breakfast. The man had not seen the canyon; but at least he had been there.

These, of course, are the exceptional visitors. The vast majority come to look and exclaim and travel on. And while the trail trips offer the main attraction there are plenty of other things to do which amuse and entertain the public. There are the rim drives from the Indian Watchtower at Desert View Point on the east, to Hermit's Rest on the west. There are explanatory walks and talks given daily by the men in the Park Service. There is Hopi House and the somewhat brief and cursory Indian dances held late every afternoon; and as most of the spectators have never seen Indian dances or heard Indian songs, these seem to them to be genuine enough. And there are museums and exhibitions and models and displays of scientific and semi-scientific nature. There is a good research library, a naturalists' workshop, and a nightly campfire talk on some phase of Southwesterniana. There are rim walks and trails and numerous benches where one may sit and contemplate the canyon at his feet. There are the tame deer, always looking for food, and there are the numerous other species of mammals, not to mention birds, reptiles, and amphibians if you but know where to look.

The swallow and the vulture seem to be the two birds most at ease at the Grand Canyon. The swallow skims past your head, startlingly close, and then "peels off" into space as he sails nonchalantly over the rim. The great brink holds no terrors for him. It is bird heaven. The swallow is so at home that he sleeps on the foot trails along the rim at night, and if you stroll in the dark you feel guilty in disturbing him. The large black vulture appears to be a small bird as he floats lazily, effortlessly, out over the embayments along the rim. At times he seems to hang motionless in the air, traveling hardly at all, until one or two flaps of his powerful wings carry him on in his course of concentric circles while his eye never ceases to scout for carrion. There are one hundred and eighty species of birds at the Grand Canyon and if you were a bird you would probably be there too. A lot of nonsense has been talked about the inability of birds to fly the ten to twelve miles separating the two rims. There were supposed to be down drafts and tricky air currents and air pockets that pulled the birds to their doom. This foolishness was ended when a red-backed junco walked into a bird trap on the South Rim on December 16, 1932. He was promptly tagged by the ranger-naturalist as H-72850 and released. And on April 20, 1933, this same junco very accommodatingly walked into a trap on the North Rim and was promptly identified. This ended all the talk of the canyon's crossing meaning death to birds.

Of the thousands of visitors there are always a few who differ with facts or who know better. One man explained to a ranger that the erosion theory was wrong and that the canyon had actually been formed when the surface of the earth cracked under pressure. His argument has as its chief support the fact that if the two rims were to be pushed together until they met, the rough edges of each would fit into a synchro-mesh. The idea was doubtless original, but its advocate had never flown over the canyon or he would have noted at once the utter fallacy of his most positive theory.

And there was the woman (and she is not alone among the "hundred million") who complained bitterly that the Park Service was blasphemous and should be punished. Not content with recriminating the local office, she even wrote to Washington about it. It seemed that she was a fundamental-ist and her ears had been affronted at the geological lecture held daily at Yavapai Point (incidentally a pleasant mile and a half walk along the rim east from El Tovar) when the lecturer gave some facts and figures. Her Bible said that the world was six thousand years old and was created in six days and it was a pretty state of affairs and an outright sacrilege when government men disputed the Bible. She wouldn't stand for it and *somebody* was going to hear about it. Somebody did, but he has not yet answered.

The ranger, of course, becomes used to the departure from the norm. He never takes any of the visitors as seriously as they take themselves. The psychology of the hundred million has a hundred million variations, but there is one point in which all agree. The canyon so dwarfs the human minimus that he simply must express his ego in some manner as a sort of psychological counterattack. He can't take it; he must find some way, instinctive, of course, to assert himself. And the usual means is to write or carve his name somewhere, somehow, so that somebody, sometime, will see it and know that he has been there and recorded that important fact.

The Santa Fe and the Fred Harvey Company have long since understood that any and all wooden benches left on the rim walks will most certainly be carved into oblivion. They seem to have found a compromise method of at least retarding this. All wooden benches are covered with a kind of heavy and extremely durable canvas. You can't carve your name in it. But it will take pencil or ink, and every bench along the South Rim is written on over every available space. People sign their names or print them, and usually give the date of their visit and their home town. When the canvas is sufficiently autographed by the visitors, and shows signs of wearing out, it is taken off and put in the incinerator, and a fresh canvas is put on the bench. It will be sure to have fifty names on it by nightfall. It is a curious phenomenon, and one that is humanly unavoidable. Of course, there are people who come to the Grand Canyon and react to it without the almost universal obsession to put their names on record except in the hotel register. But these people are greatly in the minority. The hundred million simply must assert their egos with a force as driving and as compelling as the instinctive urge which made the first animal life in the Algonkian rocks, two billion years ago near Bright Angel Creek, divide itself from a one-celled creature into a two-celled creature and thus begin the whole evolutionary chain.

The psychology of the hundred million is not strange at all. It is natural. Among the thousands of inscriptions on the canvas-covered benches there are many that run something like this:

Joe and Josie Doakes
227 Wotta Street
Paterson, N. J.
Here 3/7/28— Write to us and we'll write to you.

But what for, Joe and Josie? What for?

V

Land of the Sky Blue Water

Where Nothing Ever Happens

THERE is a sunny peaceful place on earth, in Arizona, in fact, where nothing ever happens. And as in all such idyllic spots far from the madding crowd, something usually violent is going on all the time. But it seldom shows on the surface.

If you have never been to Supai the chances are that you'd like to go. Everybody who has ever been there raves about it. There is nothing else like it in the United States, perhaps in the world. And since it is within the boundaries of Grand Canyon National Park, it is, supposedly, no trick at all to get there. Yet it takes a full day to make the journey from Grand Canyon village; you start about six in the morning and it is four or five o'clock in the afternoon before you reach your destination. And it is a trip of only fifty miles.

About thirty-five miles of this can be done in your own car, though it is inadvisable to do it unless you are used to battling poor roads. Moreover, you will have to leave your car at Hilltop where the Topocoba Trail begins, and as there is absolutely nothing at Hilltop your car will have to stand exposed to the elements for the three to five days that you are thousands of feet below in Cataract Canyon, or Havasu Falls or Supai—all the same place. (In passing, it should be mentioned that this is not the same Cataract Canyon which played such havoc with the various river parties; the same names are used for different places frequently in the West.) It is therefore wiser to arrange your trip with the Fred Harvey officials at Grand Canyon so that you travel to Hilltop in the mail truck. A Havasupai drives the truck to the head of the Topocoba Trail twice a week and your Indian atmosphere begins the moment you leave Grand Canyon village.

The young Havasupai Indian, a gentleman with the un-Indian name of Foster Marshall, has been driving this route for several years and it is probable that he will be doing so for some time. He is understandably proud of his record, for no matter how bad the weather, he has always brought the mail through. He whips the Ford truck through mud and picks his way over rocks with true automotive skill. You will have several hours to spend with Foster Marshall in the cab of the truck, and you will learn a little Havasupai speech. The road, which begins as pavement at Grand Canyon village, becomes dirt, mud, tracks, rocks, and finally two tire marks in a small canyon. The last fifteen miles is slow going and then you are at Hilltop.

This is the jumping-off place. The Topocoba Trail, up which Father Garces worked his way in 1776, is unmistakable. And far below as the ground falls away at your feet is a great gash in the earth. It is Lee Canyon, supposedly named for the renegade Mormon John Doyle Lee (who was never actually here, although the story persists that he hid for three years among the Havasupais), and it winds and cuts deep into Arizona's red earth.

You eat your Fred Harvey lunch and drink from your canteen and watch Foster Marshall unload the mail sacks from the truck. You wonder why so much mail goes to Supai until you are told that most of the sacks contain crated foodstuffs as there is no store of any kind at the tiny community far down in the canyon. There is no sign of life on the Topocoba Trail but Foster Marshall is confident that the pack train will arrive momentarily, and of course he is right. Around a bend come four burros and two Indians on horseback with extra horses for you and your party. The horses are Indian ponies, scrawny, docile, and tough, and the little burros are servile and resigned to their jobs. All conversation is in Havasupai. One of the men is "Mac" who has come up the trail to be your guide. The other is Toby to whom Foster Marshall consigns the mail. Then Foster climbs into the truck and drives away to Grand Canyon village. You are alone in a strange world with strange people who speak a soft guttural language. Mac, who is fat, smiling, and sporting a bright red shirt, comes over to you and says something that sounds exactly like, "*Umpha-ko-do-thwali-ntah-kyen.*"

You smile in your ignorance and offer him an orange left over from your lunch. He takes it and stuffs it inside his shirt. What country is this, you wonder, and then you realize this is a strange land called America. Toby, meanwhile, is loading the saddlebags of mail onto the patient little burros. In a half hour or so you get the idea that the pack train is about ready to start for Supai. Mac tries again, this time in English which he can speak reasonably well, and he says, "Thees wan is your horse. He sick." Whereupon he leaves it up to you to consider whether you look like a man who would be expected to ride a sick horse, or whether the sick horse is expected to die under you and toss you off the precipitous trail. There being no alternative, you mount. The horse is unmoved.

Toby mounts; Mac mounts; the loaded burros walk to the head of the trail. Everything has started except you and your sick horse. You use horse talk and horse persuasion, but apparently he is good and sick for he just stands.

"See—I tol' you," says Mac, smiling.

"I think he just died, Mac," you say. Now Mac has quite a sense of humor, but it is never your kind.

"No. He still livin'," says Mac, and he speaks to the horse

in Havasupai. It turns its head and looks at him. "Now you tell him to giddap," says Mac.

"Giddap," you say, but your heart isn't in it.

"Kick 'im," advises Mac. "Kick 'im hard right in the belly."

"I can't kick a sick horse, Mac—not even in the belly."

"He ain't sick," says Mac. "I get words mixed up. I say sick when I mean lazy an' lazy when I mean sick. He lazy. Kick 'im hard."

You try a few peremptory kicks, and slowly the horse walks to the trail.

"Jus' keep kickin' 'im," advises Mac, riding ahead, and immediately the descent begins. The Topocoba zigzags and follows ledges, skirts sheer precipices, and finally reaches the floor of Lee Canyon. Most of the journey of fifteen miles is in canyon bottom and dry washes, but there are a few hazardous spots where the going is decidedly steep and tricky. Deeper and deeper into the depths of the earth goes the trail with the canyon walls rising ever higher. Occasionally the main canyon is joined by side clefts and fissures. When you look back, the land is a maze of rocky defiles and to get out of this place alone would not be easy. You recall the adventures of the Ives's expedition of 1857 and you appreciate them more fully. And as for Father Garces in 1776, coming in alone over the Walapai trail and finding his way back over the baffling terrain that you are now descending—well, of such mettle are heroes. The red cliffs refract the sun's rays and the trip is hot. Once or twice the stench of dead animals permeates the air. Everything is rocks and sand and the desert flora of the lower Sonoran life zone—burro brush, cat's claw, sagebrush, mesquite, yucca, and varieties of cactus.

After four hours in the saddle, or possibly five, almost all of which has been at a slow walk with rarely a jog-trot or a lope to break the monotony, the canyon bends abruptly and you see cottonwood trees, the first green things in miles and a sure sign of water. At last you have reached the beginnings of Havasupailand. A clear bubbling creek comes out of the sand from nowhere and the growth becomes lush. There are reeds, willows, and many more cottonwood trees. Small fields of corn and squash and sunflowers take the place of the dry sandy wash. There are peach trees and apricot trees. Everything is rich and burgeoning, although the canyon is narrow and deep between its sheer red walls.

The first of the natives greet you. They are stocky brown-skinned people for the most part, with ready smiles and shining white teeth. You recall the Havasupai words that you learned in the mail truck.

"Tchew ko-mew," you say in an attempt to be pleasantly casual to a man coming toward you on horseback. He smiles back and says, "Hallo, butch," and rides on.

You are justly startled. You have come to a place as canyon-locked as Mr. Wells's Country of the Blind; you have come to an American Shangri-La; you have come to the end of the earth—and a citizen responds to your careful native greeting with "Hallo, butch." And that, you will discover, is a typical anomaly of Supai. In some respects it is the most remote civilization in North America, difficult to reach, and quite untouched; in other respects, modernity and slang and the twentieth century have also found their way down the tortuous trail. A native custom of 1400 will be enacted by an adolescent girl while she reads Life magazine. In her first puberty ceremony Deanna Spoonhead (whose Indian name is really Kokadiaba, meaning The-Girl-Who-Eats-Too-Many-Piñons) will not be allowed to touch meat, scratch herself, or see the males of her own age; and she will be put in seclusion for five days at the first evidence of her maturity. But there was nothing in the Havasupai code of five hundred years ago that forbade her to look at Eric Schaal's photographs of "The Great Electro-Mechanical Brain," and Deanna Spoonhead likes pictures.

Supai is a beautiful remote oasis with its roots embedded in the soil of pure Indian culture, and its flowers blooming from the stimulus of the twentieth century.

The pack train winds on to the Indian village which is not a village in the American sense, but really a series of small farms, their boundaries contiguous. There are small elliptical huts made of rocks and mud and cottonwood logs which seem to be the most popular type of dwelling. There are also a number of incongruous and ugly one-room frame shacks having a door and a couple of windows—cabins that look as if Uncle Tom might have inhabited one of them just before the Civil War. These don't seem to be used at all. Later you discover that the government has built these misplaced cabins as a kind of Havasupai housing project. Since the Havasupais have never lived in houses, they stick to their huts and brush shelters, and sometimes store food and keep domestic animals in the houses or else abandon them altogether.

As you reach the end of your journey the trail crosses and recrosses the blue sparkling Havasu Creek. And at each ford the water seems to become more and more blue. Travertine in the water is supposed to be the scientific answer and the name of the Havasupai country, the Land of the Sky Blue Water, is no misnomer.

Ahead you see a few small frame houses painted white. They are the post office and agent's residence, the hospital, and the school. This is the civic center and heart of Supai. Here all things come and any emergency may be expected. The agent in this peaceful little retreat where nothing ever happens puts in a good sixteen-hour day. But we'll come to the life of that overworked man in good time. As you ride up to the houses along a lane of soft earth lined with cottonwood trees and bordered with green fields you note that the canyon has widened perceptibly. This is the heart of the oasis whose life is dependent upon the blue waters of Havasu Creek. And high on a rocky ledge of the canyon walls stand two monolithic towers left by the erosion that created the canyon ten or twelve million years ago. They are huge shafts of red sandstone, the same stuff as makes up the Grand Canyon's Redwall. They appear to be natural sentinels petrified for all time, and the Havasupais revere them as gods. They are called the king and the queen, or the prince and the princess, depending upon your preference for translation from the Havasupai language which belongs to the Yuman division of Indian tongues.

These two giant pillars of red rock hold and guard the destiny of the brown-skinned people who live constantly within their sight. According to George Wharton James, who wrote several books on the Grand Canyon area about 1900, the Havasupai names for these two gods are Hue-pu-keh-eh and Hue-gli-i-wa, and according to H. G. Franse of the Fred Harvey Company who visited the Land of the Sky Blue Water in 1938, their names can be freely spelled Wiggle-ee and Wiggle-eye. One is a god and one is a goddess and when you look at them it is possible to tell which is which. Wiggle-ee, the lady, has a rounded form and a suggestion of curves about her rocky figure. Wiggle-eye, the man, is taller and more severely erect. Moreover, he stands at a pinnacle and his wife is just behind him. According to the legendry of the tribe, these figures were once a chief and his spouse who decided to leave the canyon for pastures new. Tochopa, the granddaddy of Havasupai gods and the all-powerful one, saw them in the nick of time and turned them both to stone as a warning to all good Havasupais never to follow the call of wanderlust but to remain forever in the god-given canyon that is to be theirs for eternity. So, to this day, Wiggle-ee and

Wiggle-eye are petrified warnings to the faithful to keep peace with Tochopa and preserve the sanctity of their little valley. All will be well as long as the two monolithic recalcitrants watch over their brown-skinned children, but should one or both of them ever fall, it will portend the end of the Land of the Sky Blue Water and the end of the Havasupais' days on earth. As it is unlikely that erosion can cause them to topple within a few thousand years, the tribe is reasonably safe. And perhaps by that time the legend will be revised so as to have a less tragic and fatalistic ending.

Under the watching eyes of Wiggle-ee and Wiggle-eye you arrive at the post office and home of the government agent. The Indian population of Supai is a little more than two hundred. The white population is usually three—the agent, his wife, and a registered nurse.

It is late in the afternoon when you arrive and the long shadows are spreading across the fertile fields. You are glad to part company with your Indian pony, but whether he be "sick" or "lazy," he has done a good job of picking his way over a rough trail.

At the post office you discover there is much activity. Both the agent and his wife are busy sorting the mail and crated goods. Your arrival is accepted but of no importance. Several dozen Indians will be waiting for the post-office window to open. You are a bit surprised at their eagerness. It is unlike the Indian to be excited over the arrival of mail. But they are apparently anxious and they crowd about the doorway of the tiny post office which is said to be the most remote and inaccessible in the United States. The agent assures them—"Yes, a package for Lemuel Paya, another for Dirty Face Siyuja, a crate of oranges for Melvyn Sinyella, a box of canned goods for Ora Little Jim, some cigarettes for Willie Uqualla"—and so on. Whereupon Lemuel, and Dirty Face, and Melvyn, and Ora, and Willie, and a dozen or more others, are pleasantly satisfied and they mount their horses and ride off to their respective homes (nobody ever goes anywhere in Supai except on horseback), leaving the packages and boxes in the post office. They hadn't come to get them; they just wanted to make sure they were there. One reason for this is that most of the packages have come C.O.D. Now Willie Uqualla may not have the dollar and some cents required to claim the cigarettes he ordered last week. Once he knows they have arrived he can claim them any time, and the cigarettes may remain in the post office for a month or two until Willie finds some way of earning a dollar or so. But at least Willie has peace of mind; the purchase is there. It has been a busy day.

Being established as a guest in Supai means being put in the hospital. Next door to the post office is a frame building with a screened porch, a bathroom with plumbing, and seven beds. The house has a perpetual odor of iodoform and you may have any one of the seven beds you wish because the Indians never use the hospital. You choose the bed on the screen porch as it is pleasant to sleep out of doors in the warm night air and the odor of iodoform is less prevalent. You may have no fear that an emergency case will arrive before morning. Accident and tragedy never follow the conventional pattern in Supai. Something will probably happen during the night but it will not concern you.

About ten o'clock the agent turns off the motor which supplies the power, and a candle or a flashlight will be the only illumination thenceforth. But after five hours in the saddle, you will be happy to lie in bed in the screened darkness of the porch and listen to the night sounds of Supai. A horse whinnies and far up (or down) the canyon another horse answers. Then silence. A dog trots by. More silence. A jackass heehaws far away. Deep silence—finally broken by a sound that you can't identify. It is a kind of ripping or tearing and then munching. At last you make sense out of it; a horse or a mule is eating the grass just outside your porch. During the night he will eat his way along the lane for several hundred yards, gradually working his way out of earshot. Then complete, profound silence. Just as you are falling asleep you hear the soft thud-thud of horse's hoofs galloping along the lane. The rider stops at the agent's house. You hear him clump up to the entrance. After a moment there are voices. You snap a flashlight on your watch. It is one-thirty in the morning. The agent and the Indian talk. You can't make it out. You sit up in bed and peer through the screen. By the arc of the agent's flashlight you see that he has partially dressed. The Indian has remounted. The agent swings himself up behind him. Together they ride off double, and bareback, into the warm night, redolent of damp grass, horse sweat, and iodoform. Something has happened. You wonder what. It is all very mystifying. Thinking about it you decide this is a typical night in Supai, and it is. You sleep.

Sunday in Havasu Falls

SUNDAY comes once a week in America, be it in the land of the Sky Blue Water or Cicero Falls, Vermont. In fact, the Sunday in Cicero Falls, as portrayed in the musical comedy *Bloomer Girl* is no more quaint and nonetheless American than Sunday in Havasu Falls, Arizona. Both communities recognize the Lord's Day, genuflect, and pay homage. There is a difference, but it is a variation in method rather than theory. Cicero Falls may sing *Beulah Land* or *Shall We Gather at the River*, while more than three thousand miles to the Southwest, Havasu Falls sings:

> *Baya ha tigavaikawi*
> *Baya ha tigavaikawi*
> *Gaki yapa taopa hikyumuu*
> *JESUS inyivame e,*

and perhaps the same end is achieved.

Mr. Lonnie Hardin was the government agent when I last saw Supai and he courteously asked me if I should like to attend church services. Following the cliché—when in Havasupailand do as the Havasupais do—I agreed that I should like nothing better, although the number of times I had attended formally orthodox religious services could be counted on the fingers of one hand. So, as became two Christian gentlemen on a Sunday morning, whether they found themselves in Vermont or Arizona, we strolled to church.

Services are held in the schoolhouse. We were not early, but we were the first to arrive. In fact, Mr. Hardin rang the schoolhouse bell. This "terrible summons" aroused a stalwart, sober, and good-looking gentleman named Jim Crook. Preacher Crook had been sleeping on a bed under a near-by cottonwood tree, resting and gathering strength for the sermon he was about to deliver. He wore a pair of dark trousers and a green shirt. His hair was black, his skin was brown, and his teeth were white. He must have weighed two hundred pounds. On the whole his serious and dignified mien inspired respect and confidence. As he approached the house of God he evinced no interest whatever in me, a stranger, but said, "Good morning" to Mr. Hardin.

"Mr. Crook, this is Mr. Corle," said Mr. Hardin. "Mr. Corle, this is Mr. Crook."

"Good morning, Mister," said Mr. Crook.

"Good morning, Crook," said Mr. Corle.

"Mr. Crook is our preacher," said Mr. Hardin.

"I'm happy to know you, Mr. Crook," I said.

"Yep," said Mr. Crook.

There was an awkward pause, yet there seemed to be nothing any of us could say.

"I—ah—I've just arrived," I said, hesitatingly, to Mr. Crook. A more banal remark could not have been conceived, and unless Mr. Crook were blind and deaf, he could not help knowing that superfluous fact.

"Yep," said Mr. Crook.

"He came in last night," said Mr. Hardin, not being much of a help.

"With the pack train," I said, although how else I might have got there except by parachute I cannot imagine.

"Yep," said Mr. Crook.

"Nice day," said Mr. Hardin, and added, "Mr. Corle is a writer," although a relation between the weather and my profession seemed irrelevant to me.

"Acts, Chapter nine," said Mr. Crook.

"Acts, Chapter nine," said Mr. Hardin to me.

"Oh—Acts, Chapter nine," I said, gayly and self-consciously.

"Yep," said Mr. Crook.

By that time I was more than ill at ease; I was embarrassed. And I was embarrassed for the worst of all reasons—no reason at all, unless it could be that I had never chatted with a minister of the gospel just before he preached. Such a state of mind invariably demands a defense mechanism of some sort. The obvious method is self-assertion. I at once followed that line of psychological least resistance. I did a stupid and egoistic and idle thing—yet I followed instinctively the laws of human nature. I asserted myself. I drew out my wallet and did something that was so far from my intention that it was done as a drunkard drives a car—without thought. I opened my wallet and presented Mr. Crook with my card.

He took it and he looked at it. Probably (I thought) nobody ever gave him a personal card before. And I, who have been proud of myself for behaving well with Indians from Isleta to Oraibi, from Oaxaca to Montana, was acting like a damned fool. Mr. Crook put my card in his pants pocket. He said nothing.

"It's time for church," said Mr. Hardin, charitably.

"Yep," said Mr. Crook.

Both walked into the schoolhouse and I followed.

Mr. Crook went to the teacher's desk, took from a drawer a green cloth, and tacked it up over the blackboard. From a closet he took a small squatty wooden cross, standing upright on a wooden base, and plunked it on the desk. The stage was set.

Mr. Hardin and I sat in cramped discomfort in students' desks intended for ten-year-olds.

"Where is the congregation?" I asked Mr. Hardin in a whisper.

"His kids will be here in a minute," he said. "Nobody else ever comes."

And he was right. Three young Havasupai children entered from the rear almost at once. One was a girl of nine or ten, and the others were boys about eight and seven. They sat down at the rear of the room and the boys were all too eagerly waiting for their big sister to finish perusing a comic book about *Bat Man*. The three gave no heed to Mr. Crook whatever.

"What denomination is this?" I asked Mr. Hardin in a whisper.

"E-pis-co-pal-ian," he whispered back.

"*Ee-ga-yava-kiwa-sa-do-ee—*" intoned Mr. Crook. Mr. Hardin was seriously attentive. I was the same.

"I now read the Bible in Glish," said Mr. Crook. "Acts, Chapter nine."

A pause. Mr. Crook took a deep breath and began to read very slowly.

"And Saul get *brith ga-ntha* out from—*slawga ajawai* the *dleth-ka-wa* Lord went to priest." He looked up and said: "That mean Saul he not trust God." Then studying the book, he continued, "And *dezeh gawa baya* Damascus to *syngo-wa*, *gla-wo-so* men or women *bla-ga* Jerusalem." With a pause he appended, "That mean the same thing."

And then:

"And then he *gawa-ko-no lini-tchew-ga* Damascus *gletka ko-la-meglla-ee-tlak-do-ee-ya* heaven."

The sermon continued in this slowly paced guttural speech, punctuated only by the rattle of a turned page of *Bat Man*

[252]

coming from the rear. At times Preacher Crook would vary the service by singing a hymn. In this the congregation was supposed to join, but Mr. Hardin was unable to sing in Havasupai and I was unable to sing in any language. And there were no notes printed in *Bat Man*.

Once during the sermon, Preacher Crook broke the narrative of his story and spoke directly to his daughter. She put *Bat Man* aside, and left the schoolroom. Mr. Hardin, who understood enough Havasupai, whispered to me, "He sent her home."

"Is he displeased?" I asked.

"No. He told her to go get a card for you."

"A card?"

"Yes—you gave him yours. He sent for his."

The sermon continued, and in the course of a few minutes more it turned out that Saul was completely converted to the teaching of Jesus and that he defied all recalcitrants. There was a hairbreadth escape when Saul was let down a wall in a basket, and finally Barabbas spoke up for Saul's cause to the apostles; and Saul, entirely vindicated, preached boldly at Damascus in the name of Jesus. It was not an unpleasant story at all, and the novelty of hearing it in the Havasupai language with something resembling English interpolations for my benefit was interesting and flattering.

Mr. Crook sang another hymn, and the services were over. He took down the green cloth and returned the cross to the closet and the nave was a schoolroom again.

Miss Crook came forward and gave her father a card and Mr. Crook gave the card to me. I thanked him and said that I had enjoyed his sermon and that I was sure he was doing good work. He thanked me, and I put his card in my wallet. I carry it there permanently for it is the only card I have ever received from an Indian and am always glad to produce it on demand for anyone who doubts the story. The card reads simply:

JIM CROOK
Havasupai, Arizona

and down in one corner: *"via Grand Canyon."* Mr. Crook, I learned, was one of the few members of the tribe who have wandered from the native heath. He traveled as far as Phoenix, and there was converted to Episcopalianism which he brought back with him. Every Sunday with calm and determined zeal he preaches. The fact that nobody ever listens bothers him not at all.

After church, it still being early Sunday morning, I walked on through Havasupailand, considering the anomaly of coming to this remote corner of the United States which comparatively few Americans had ever seen, and running abruptly into an aboriginal society whose roots, pagan and pure, put forth not the flower of an Indian culture, but a Jewish story conceived almost two thousand years ago on the other side of the world.

All that was needed to complete this farrago of crossed religions and races would be for me to preach the creation myth as Havasupai literature conceived it back to them in English. The story is not a departure from the creation legend as told by most Southwestern Indians, but it is of interest as it brings the Grand Canyon into the story in a way which Navajo and Apache versions do not. As it is not a written story, it must be heard directly from one of the tribal patriarchs, such as Jim Gvetka or Watahamogie or possibly Billy Burro (not Jim Crook, for he will tell you the Biblical version), or you can find it ably told in print by George Wharton James, Edward S. Curtis, or Leslie Spier. In fact, it has even appeared in the *Saturday Evening Post.*

In brief here is the Havasupai Book of Genesis:

Before there were any people on the earth there were two gods, Tochopa of goodness and Hokomata of evil. Tochopa had a daughter (beautiful, of course) named Pu-keh-eh, and he hoped that she might produce human beings and become the mother of all living. Hokomata was determined that no such thing should take place, and he decided to cover the world with a great flood. Whereupon each god went to work in his own way. Tochopa felled a great tree and hollowed out the trunk. Hokomata, meanwhile was causing terrible storms, and the water was covering the earth. Pu-keh-eh was hidden by her father in the hollow tree trunk, and when the water rose and flooded the earth, she was secure in her improvised boat—which, of course, recalls Noah's ark.

After a long period of time the flood waters began to fall. Mountain peaks emerged. Rivers were created; and one of them cut the great gashing fissure which became the Grand Canyon. The log bearing Pu-keh-eh came to rest on the new earth. Pu-keh-eh stepped forth and beheld an empty world of drenched lands, rushing rivers, great canyons, and heavy mists. She was alone on the earth.

At last the mists lifted and the land became dry, and a great golden sun rose in the east and warmed the earth. As Pu-keh-eh lay on the soft ground the sun's rays touched her and caused her to conceive. In time she gave birth to a male child and with this phenomenon Pu-keh-eh knew that her father's wish was coming true. Later she lay beside a waterfall and this time water caused her to conceive and she gave birth to a girl. (Although the variation in detail is great, here is a virgin-birth legend used for a somewhat different purpose than in Christian mysticism.) From the union of these two mortal children (a Havasupai Adam and Eve) came all the people on the earth. The first were the Havasupais, and the voice of Tochopa spoke to them and told them to live forever in peace in their canyon of good earth and pure water where there would always be plenty for all. They have been the happiest people on the earth ever since. Persecution, crucifixion, baptism, torture, preaching, conversion, immersion, ascension, in fact, all Christian manifestations are alien to them, for they find such psychoses totally unnecessary.

That is the story you should really hear on Sunday in Havasu Falls.

Where Did Robinson Crusoe Go with Friday on Saturday Night?

WHITE men have been finding their way into Havasupailand since 1776 when Padre Garces was the first outlander to enter the hidden canyon. There were gaps in the eighteenth and nineteenth centuries when white men failed to appear for many years at a time. Garces in 1776, Lieutenant Ives in 1858, Dr. Elliott Coues in 1881, and Frank Cushing a few years later, made the only expeditions of importance up to the twentieth century.

As the years went by the Havasupai people remained an isolated oasis of Indian culture unchanged by the westward movement of the white race. It was a land where time stood still, peace and beauty reigned supreme, and nothing as radical and as naïve as scientific progress broke the aboriginal routine. It is the modern Havasupai's boast that he has never killed a white man. This may have been changed by the Selective Service Act and World War II for the draft of manpower reached the remotest corner of Arizona and some Havasupai boys may have seen combat. If so, and if they were in France or Belgium or Germany in 1944 and 1945, it may well be that the Havasupai record of never taking a white life has been broken by the demands of the white race itself. But up until 1943 at least the Havasupais lived at peace. Occasionally they were raided by other Indians, particularly the Apaches, during the eighteenth and nineteenth centuries. The warlike Apache was after plunder and women. The rocky bastions of the Grand Canyon made raids difficult. The Havasupai likes to tell with understandable pride of his defense of his goods and his women and of his courageous exploits of driving the Apaches away. This would be pleasant to accept, but the truth is that the Havasupais, never bellicose, retreated into their labyrinthian canyons and side-canyons, and wore the Apaches out in a game of hide-and-seek. A few Havasupai girls were captured and taken away by the Apaches, but the marauders were severely beaten (supposedly) at their last foray. This was many years ago, and Captain Burro, father of Billy Burro whom you may meet, is credited with the victory. As the story goes he fired the only rifle in the canyon and scared the bad Apaches away. Anyone who knows anything about the Apaches may well smile. For the Apaches, along with the Sioux, were fighters from the word go. They feared nobody—red or white—and their unswerving policy was victory or death. But one-shot Captain Burro basked for many years in the guise of a great warrior. He plodded along on his mule at a jaunty gait and wore his old and battered hat with a rake-helly air, for he was the sum total of the armed forces of Havasupailand and he knew it, something comparable to the Liechtenstein Army. Nature never intended the tribe to be warlike and it never was; but it could boast.

Fighting over material wealth or religious systems, stories of avarice and greed, concepts of sin and the pangs of a conditioned conscience never troubled the Havasupais. There was usually enough for everybody to eat, everybody got married (but never to a relative nearer than third cousin), the weather was never too hot or too cold, the fields were fertile and there was game above on the mesas, children played all day in the sun and in the laughing blue water, life was to be enjoyed and what more could anyone ask? It was, and it still is, a happy place. Take no preconceived notions with you and you'll enjoy it; go looking for Utopia or any form of escape and you'll be disappointed.

After the twentieth century, a few white men went to Havasupailand for material reasons. Two of the most disappointed were a Mr. Johnson and a Mr. Mooney.

As you walk downstream, from what may be called for purposes of identification, Supai village, you will come to four magnificent waterfalls. The gurgling blue Cataract Creek (or Havasu Creek—names are not too specific in this country of ease) crashes over Navajo Falls, Bridal Veil (or Havasu) Falls, Mooney Falls, and Beaver Falls. If you go a few miles farther you will come to the confluence of Havasu Creek and the Colorado River deep in the Grand Canyon. It is not an easy trip, but as far as the crest of Mooney's Falls you can make it on horseback. From there on, it is a hike to the Colorado.

These falls are not ordinary—they are extraordinary. Navajo Falls drops one hundred and forty feet, a little less than Niagara. A quarter of a mile downstream, Bridal Veil plunges one hundred and seventy feet, and that is a little more than Niagara. Mooney, a concentrated tongue of terrific power, drops about two hundred feet. And Beaver, according to Randall Henderson, editor of *The Desert Magazine*, is a cascade rather than a fall, quite as spectacular as any of the rest. Due to the presence of carbonates of lime the water is often as blue as bluing. The lime, precipitated from the water, has formed huge spills of travertine at each waterfall.

A miner named Mooney was more interested in precious metals than the beauty of the place. He arrived about the turn of the century and the smiling Havasupais gladly guided him to the most likely sites for what he (for reasons inexplicable to them) seemed to want—material wealth. Mooney kept his appointment in Samarra by lowering himself down a bluff on a rope just below the falls that now bear his name. He was unable to get back and the Havasupais were unable to rescue him. After a day or two of dangling agony he either slipped or the rope broke and he fell to his death on the sharp rocks far below. Only his name remains.

Mr. Johnson had better luck; at least he lived longer. After Mooney's abortive efforts, from 1900 to 1906, something less than fifty tons of high-grade lead and silver ore were somehow packed out. It cost more than it was worth. In 1906 Mr. W. I. Johnson became president of the Northern Arizona Lead and Zinc Mining Company, which offered 500,000 shares of stock at a par value of one dollar each. Interesting figures. The stock can be bought for less than par today if you are interested. Mr. Johnson had some elaborate ideas for the development of the project, one of which was an aerial tramway. It has never come into existence, although the Fred Harvey Company has also considered it. Havasupailand offers insuperable barriers for practical mining and for tourist trade. A tramway or a funicular would facilitate mining operations, and would make it possible for tourists to be deposited in the canyon depths and hauled out again none the worse for wear. The day may come; and when it does Havasupailand will never be quite the same. This will be good or bad, desirable or not, according to individual reactions.

Between Bridal Veil and Mooney Falls you will find the base of operations (one cabin) of the Northern Arizona Lead and Zinc Mining Company. The door is askew, the windows are gone, papers are scattered about—only the prospecting spirit of Mooney and the organizing zeal of Johnson remain to haunt the spot. Nevertheless, as late as 1943, when World War II demanded raw materials, there was a renaissance of the old claims. In spite of prohibitive costs, men were willing to try again to extract wealth from the Grand Canyon country. E. B. Stephens and James D. Culbertson of San Francisco, as principals in the Havasu Lead and Zinc Mining Company moved equipment down the long tortuous trail to Mooney Falls. The objective this time was chiefly vanadium, but lead and zinc as well. There was much enthusiasm in 1943 over the old Johnson mine, for a war had to be won and strategic materials were essential. Cost was dwarfed by price. But that was 1943. Now the war is over. Want to buy some stock today in Havasu Lead and Zinc? The Havasupais are not interested.

On your return from your walk to the various waterfalls you will pass the residence of Jim Crook. It is a mud-and-brush shelter and you will see Mrs. Crook and the children at home. If it is Sunday, Mr. Crook will probably be sleeping on his bed under his cottonwood tree and you, having heard Acts, Chapter Nine, will wisely not disturb him. You pass the school (and church) and return to your home at the hospital.

In this remote world there are certain of the white man's inventions which cannot penetrate. It has been said that somebody tried to bring a piano down the Topocoba Trail, that it slipped to one side of the mule carrying it, and went crashing over a cliff, taking the mule with it. I believe the story is untrue. It is certain, however, that at least one sewing machine has been packed in for I have seen it. But no automobiles or tractors or airplanes can make it. There is telephone communication between the agent's residence and Grand Canyon; the agent has a radio, but reception is none too good; and as for juke boxes, there are blessedly none.

Imagine then my surprise to hear one night about eleven o'clock as I lay in bed (all lights out as the power was turned off by the agent when he went to bed) either a radio or a gramophone. This instrument suddenly cut the pungent night air with its strident music, and it was a tune that was somehow familiar.

A voice sang in a rasping nasal chorus beginning plainly enough with the words, "Where did . . ." and I couldn't catch the rest. It could be a few hundred yards away or even farther, as sound travels clearly in the quiet night air boxed in by the sheer canyon walls. All doubt about it being a radio was soon removed, for, with no commercial announcement to affront anyone, the song was played over again. There was no doubt now that it was a gramophone and that somebody liked the selection enough to repeat it. And this time I definitely heard the words "there must be wild women." I hoped the unseen audience would play it a third time so that I could catch some more.

The audience did.

The record was played over and over again. By the seventh or eighth playing, in spite of the unhuman screeches and the fact that the record must have been played thin, I got the whole chorus except for one or two doubtful words which could be surmised. I thought of writing it down, but my nightbound host made that unnecessary by immediately playing it an eighth or ninth consecutive time. There was no doubt now, and even with my unmusical ear I sang to myself along with the artist:

> *Where did Robinson Crusoe go*
> *With Friday on Saturday night?*
> *Every Saturday night*
> *They would start out at eight*
> *And on Sunday morning*
> *They'd come staggering home.*
> *Now 'twas an island of wild men*
> *In a cannibal region*

WHERE DID ROBINSON CRUSOE GO?

But where there are wild men
There must be wild women!
So where did Robinson Crusoe go
With Friday on Saturday night?

And on and on far into the night, until I lost all count, Robinson Crusoe set forth with Friday, both of them out for no good but having one roaring hilarious time come Sunday morning. Somewhere around the fortieth consecutive playing, I managed to sleep.

Utopia—it's wonderful.

One Mind in Indian Time

No MATTER how calm and placid are the days in Havasu Falls, no two are alike. In a sense you are in a country of children, and something is likely to happen at any time of the day or night as the overworked agent can well testify. While I spent five days there, Havasupailand had a birth, a death, a horse-race, a rodeo, nightly gambling, a marriage, a divorce, a fire, a starving baby due to absence of mother's milk, a maturation ceremony for an adolescent girl, a sweat-bath cure for men (a cure for any complaint no matter what the ailment may be), and innumerable accidents from serious wounds to injured fingers. And the agent may expect a call at any time of the day or night for anything from obstetrical supervision to lending somebody a pound of coffee or fixing a loose belt on the sewing machine.

The Havasupai mind is childlike but not childish. Mac, whose real name I never did learn, and who was my guide both ways on the Topocoba Trail, is a typical member of this tribe. He is cheerful, willing, inclined to be fat, has a dark brown skin, immaculate white teeth, and a sense of humor. He worries not at all about anything ever. His mental balance and his effortless tranquillity bring to mind the "happy moron" jingle in paraphrase:

[264]

ONE MIND IN INDIAN TIME

See the happy Havasupai,
He doesn't give a damn.
I wish I were a Havasupai.
My God! Maybe I am!

But Mac is far from a moron, and I saw no signs of idiocy, feeble-mindedness, or even mental backwardness among his people. He simply thinks and feels with values that are in contrast to those of the white world.

Mac is more or less in the horse business. He wished to rent me a horse during my stay in Supai. I didn't want a horse, having already covered a great deal of the Grand Canyon country on horse and mule where distances were great and trails steep. In Supai it was a pleasure to be able to stroll at will. But in order to be agreeable to Mac and to provide a modicum of business, I agreed to take a horse once in a while. At Mac's third or fourth solicitation I managed to make it clear that I wanted the intimacy of exploring on foot, but would like to ride a horse the next day from two in the afternoon to six or seven. That is the way any white man would have arranged it. I should have known better. That is not the Indian way. Mac was bothered about a detail—how would he know when it was two o'clock?

"Oh, just bring the horse about this time tomorrow," I said, and Mac went away.

He was back in an hour with an old alarm clock which was not running. Meanwhile I had left on foot. So Mac told the agent's wife that he wanted to be sure to know when it was two o'clock. Mrs. Hardin set the clock for him. Mac went away smiling and carrying the ticking clock. About eleven hours later, at 2 A.M., of course, it went off and woke up the whole Mac family who had to let the alarm run down as it was dark and nobody could find the means of turning it off. At two-thirty in the morning Mac arrived with my horse. The clock had been set to tell him when I wanted it. The clock told him. Ergo: he brought the horse. His logic was perfect and he went to a lot of trouble. It was very disappointing to find out after waking me that I did not want the horse at 2:30 A.M. after all. These white men! Don't know their own minds, decided Mac. But in case I should change my mind, as white men have been known to do, he tethered the horse outside my door. After he left it proceeded to whinny all the rest of the night, for it was lonely and unaccustomed to being left in such a place at such an hour. Next morning, about seven, one of Mac's kids came and got the horse. I had said from two to seven, hadn't I? Well . . . ?

But this was not the end.

During the morning the agent's wife explained to Mac that the white man has two two o'clocks during one day and one night and that they are twelve hours apart. To Mac, quite reasonably, this seemed unnecessarily complicated. Why not have just one two o'clock and be done with it? Nevertheless, he accepted it as a white man's idiosyncrasy and decided to abide by it. The clock was set again, this time for the right two o'clock, and Mac went home.

I was back at two in the afternoon—but no Mac and no horse. Around six o'clock he showed up with no horse, but smilingly carrying the alarm clock. It hadn't worked. Upon examination it turned out that even though the clock was running in good order, nobody had thought to rewind the alarm. It had rung accurately twelve hours before and Mac took it for granted that it would do it again. It hadn't, and Mac slept through the whole afternoon. Naturally he could not know when it was two o'clock. Alarm clocks were a great evil anyway, and Mac wanted me to know it. He was not in the least disturbed because he had not rented me a horse. Some other time maybe. And that was quite satisfactory to me as I had not wanted the horse in the first place. We all were simply delighted with the outcome of the whole business; and I, being a white man in an Indian world, paid Mac for the horse anyway, which is what I should have done to start with, thus avoiding the whole issue. Mac left happily with a little more money than he had when the enterprise was begun, and as he left he paused and looked critically at the silent clock and said to me, "Now, what time is it?"

"About that time," I said.

"That's right," said Mac, and cheerfully went his way, still carrying the unpredictable clock.

This incident is not told to belittle the Indian. From his point of view he had done everything within reason. I was simply impossible to please. After all, imagine living in a world where there were two two o'clocks twelve hours apart! I might just as well have requested a horse with two sets of forelegs.

And speaking of oddities in horses, would you like to see an *eohippus?* So would I. There is a story going the rounds about the "little horses" of Supai, which are said to be paleontological hangovers from the Eocene epoch of the Cenozoic era. In other words, evolution is supposed to have done what evolution never does—failed to evolve. The horse of forty million years ago was a small four-toed and then three-toed mammal, the *eohippus*, which finally evolved into the animal we know today. That any specimen of the prehistoric horse lives in the Grand Canyon country is such utter nonsense that I first thought it was somebody's joke. But the story is actually told now and then, and an *eohippus* has been exhibited in a small traveling circus. Darwin would smile and Barnum would be delighted.

This ridiculous story came about because Foster Marshall, the Havasupai driver of the mail truck between Grand Canyon village and the head of the Topocoba Trail, caught an *eohippus*—or better, caught a horse—or more accurately, roped a small wild mare. She was a perfect little horse, only forty-three inches in height, and weighed one hundred and fifty pounds. She was not a pony and not a colt for her mane, her tail, and her teeth were all those of a mature animal. Her age was estimated at four to five years. She was simply the "smallest little horse," according to Foster Marshall, that he had ever seen. So he put her in the rumbleseat of a car and took her to the town of Williams and sold her to a circus. There she became an *eohippus* and an *eohippus* she is today.

What had happened to make these little horses (others have been seen and by this time more *eohippi* may have been captured) seem to evolve backwards? The most plausible theory is that their ancestors were full-size horses about 1870 and were lost, abandoned, or strayed into the endless maze of canyons that lead into Havasupailand and the Grand Canyon. Being tough little Indian ponies to start with, they got along on the scant forage and little water, and successive generations soon adapted themselves to their environment. Foster Marshall's *eohippus* is probably the seventh or eighth generation of an average horse brought to a stage of dwarf by a rigorous and difficult land offering insufficient sustenance. In evolution, where size is a handicap, the animal grows smaller. The little horses of the Grand Canyon region are living testimonials of the Lamarckian theory of acquired characteristics. And the theory works both ways. For William Lockridge, a civil engineer, also caught an *eohippus* (not as small as Foster Marshall's), weighing three hundred pounds, and fattened her up with good food to four hundred pounds of animal. This mare produced a colt, sired by an average-size horse, and the issue became a normal Indian pony. In one generation evolution under favorable conditions, brought the *eohippus* back to modern times, skipping something like forty million years, and proving that the little horse was merely a runt, anything but an *eohippus*.

One other fallacy about the Havasupai country might be mentioned, as it, too, has led to fantastic stories. In a side canyon there is a petroglyph (a design cut or etched into rock by a sharp tool) which is said to show an Indian fighting a death battle with a type of dinosaur. This has been used as proof that man lived in Arizona a hundred million years ago. The only trouble is that if you take a good look at the petroglyph (which may well be several hundred years old) the addition of the dinosaur—if it be any sub-order of dinosauria at all, and the artist apparently wanted to portray an iguanodon—was obviously made not over twenty years ago.

Thrilling adventures in ecology and ethnology may be found in the Grand Canyon country but nothing as sensational as Sunday supplement stuff can be expected.

Among the features of Supai, however, which are not fantasies, and will reward you, are some of the crafts—notably, tanning and basketry. The men are extremely skillful in bleaching and tanning deerskins, and you can get material for some very fine moccasins, leggings, and ceremonial jackets if you wear that type of clothing. I don't. The baskets are woven by the women and are well known among collectors for their perfection and for the fact that the best of them are watertight. They are made of finely split willows and the bark of cat's claw, sometimes called devil's claw, or more technically, martynia. Among the best basket weavers are Elsie Sinyella, Nina Siyuja, Lily Burro, and Dottie Watahamogie. Designs are stylized, but usually are based upon animal and bird figures, such as the eagle, the owl, the horse, the deer, the rooster, and so on. Almost all are black on white. Often a geometrical figure is used which resembles a six-pointed star. If you ask, you'll be told this is merely a popular design having no esoteric meaning. But it is easier to tell you this than to explain the combination of economic and religious reasons behind the motif. This six-pointed figure is made for export to the Hopi, with whom the Havasupais trade, and is used by that tribe at the annual Snake Dance in Hopiland. The figure represents the six cardinal points of the Hopi compass, and the basket is important in the ceremonials conducted by the priests of the Hopi Snake Clan. The Havasupai and the Hopi have long been friendly tribes, and an old Indian trail leads from Supai easterly to the Hopi villages just beyond the Painted Desert.

Havasupai ceremonies in themselves are few. The tribe is not especially religious-minded. It doesn't need the affirmation of ritualism. The chief crops are corn, beans, peaches, melons, sunflowers, squash, and figs. Life is pleasant, and sacrifices and offerings to the gods are not required. The dance of the peach harvest in August is their only celebration of note—a kind of Thanksgiving in Havasu Falls. To this the Hopi are welcome; and occasionally an outlander Navajo, and inevitably that strangest of all creatures, the white man, will find his way to the peach harvest. I was there just ahead of this event, and I have taken it, perhaps naïvely, as a personal compliment, that the venerable chief, Watahamogie himself, invited me to return for the peach dance. I regret that I was unable to be there—but like Mac's horse, the day will come, so why worry? I learned this attitude from Watahamogie, who is either ninety-two or ninety-eight or one hundred fourteen or any other age, depending upon what number comes up first in the roulette of his mind. I told the quiet chief that I should like to return for the peach harvest but that circumstances might prevent my doing so. I made it simpler. I said, "I want to. I'll try to." Whereupon he, philosophically and typically, said, "Come this year. Come next year. Come any year." That's Havasupai.

Speaking of patriarchs ("chief" is a misnomer among most Indian tribes), I've mentioned besides Watahamogie, Captain Burro, the "militarist," and Jim Crook, the Christian. One other should not be overlooked and he is Big Jim Gvetka. There are two Jim families, Little and Big. Big Jim Gvetka is not so big physically, but he is big in prestige. H. G. Franse of the Fred Harvey Company calls Big Jim a one-man chamber of commerce. In a sense he is. His name means "Whiskers." He often wears a "stovepipe" hat and a frock coat with medals pinned to the breast. When Theodore Roosevelt visited the Grand Canyon thirty-five years ago, Big Jim decided he'd like to see a white chief. He made a trip to the South Rim and the story goes that T. R. and Big Jim became good friends. The top hat and the frock coat are said to be presents from T. R. to Big Jim, and there is no reason to doubt the story. Later Big Jim heard that another white chief was at the South Rim so he made another trip and called upon Albert, then King of the Belgians. Albert recognized Big Jim as a man of parts and property and presented him with some medals. Big Jim accepted them as a matter of course, and wore them on T. R.'s coat. Would Albert care to take a muleback ride and visit Big Jim's mud-and-brush shack and eat squashblossoms and enjoy a good sweat bath beside Havasu Creek? No? Too bad. Well—next year. Come early. Bring your wife. Bring all the Belgians. And Big Jim returned to his canyon home and Albert returned to Europe.

It may come as a surprise to most visitors that the Havasupais have a Constitution and By-laws. It may be a surprise to many of the Havasupais, too, but the document exists. Just how positively it functions is difficult to say. At least it puts the stamp of authority and legality upon tribal legislation—although I've never heard of any tribal legislation *per se*. It is, however, an example of the white man's effort to clothe Indian affairs in the dress of statecraft. If it doesn't work, it at least does no harm.

The Constitution was approved by the Assistant Secretary of the Interior on March 27, 1938, but I doubt if it is couched in language that very much concerns Watahamogie or Big Jim Gvetka or the rank and file of Havasupai citizens such as Mac or Billy Burro or Coolidge Uqualla or Willie Spoonhead. Somehow the preamble doesn't sound exactly Indian. Listen:

"We, the Havasupai Tribe of the Havasupai Reservation, Arizona, in order to build up an independent and self-directing community life; to secure to ourselves and our children all rights guaranteed to us by treaties and by Statutes of the United States; and to encourage and promote all movements and efforts for the best interests and welfare of our people, do establish this Constitution and By-laws." That's hardly the way Mac would have put it, and Mac is a typical Havasupai. Could Washington have had anything to do with this composition?

There follow various "Articles" pertaining to Territory, Membership, Elections, Referendum, Amendments, and so on, and these Articles are followed by the more specific By-laws. That the tribe willfully and by a majority vote in an election adopted this Constitution is attested by the signature of Arthur Kaska, Chairman of the Tribal Council.

Well—that's just fine. Certainly nobody objects. But I doubt if Dirty Face Siyuja and Willie Spoonhead and Ruthie Broken Rope, arguing the merits of trading some baskets to the Walapai or considering planting some new peach trees ever reach such an impasse that Willie rises and points an accusatory finger at Dirty Face and says, "I object to your statement on the grounds that it is unconstitutional," while Dirty Face, in turn, counters with, "I contest your objection and recommend you read the By-laws, Article II, Section two, paragraph seven," and Ruthie intervenes with the suggestion that Article VIII provides for amendments provided a majority vote of the Tribal Council approves and that this discussion can therefore be settled by interpreting the issue in terms of the letter of the law. No, it isn't done that way in the Indian mind. The baskets will be traded or the new peach trees will be set out. Dirty Face will reach his decision as he gambles for cigarettes with Willie, and Ruthie will decide that new land could be used for peach trees while she is listening to the forty-ninth consecutive playing of *Where Did Robinson Crusoe Go with Friday on Saturday Night?* The aboriginal mind will not function in terms of Colonial American political science.

In other words, the Indian has a mind of his own. It may be interpreted, but it is not ready to be converted.

Yet strange and new values are coming down the trail to Supai. What will the sons of Lemuel Paya and Rock Hamidreek and Billy Burro bring back after a couple of years in the infantry in the Philippines or Tokyo or the Rhine Valley? And what social changes are bound to enter Supai when Della Sinyella, who, for two years helped make airplane wings for Lockheed in California, returns, as she recently did, to her own people? Della will have learned a lot of things that are alien to Tochopa and Pu-keh-eh, and the rest of the Havasupai gods. For today Della wears slacks, a permanent wave, and paints her fingernails. Will this generation become a new Havasupai society, or will it revert to the old ways and have its babies on the dirt floor of a mud-and-brush shelter? How strongly will the white vaccination take? What will be the effect, if any, of sanitation over primitive plumbing, contraception over chance reproduction, penicillin over sweat baths? One more generation holds the answer.

Today Supai, although definitely touched by the white world, supports a society of two hundred people which was "American" before the land was called America. Perhaps nowhere else in the United States can you find a geographical and social unit which has preserved so well the aboriginal civilization of a hundred, two hundred, and five hundred years ago. They were here when Columbus sailed from Palos, and in many ways, they haven't changed; but Columbus never heard of radar in 1492, and Dickie Lamehorse, with two battle stars, can tell you all about it today.

This doubtless represents the transitional period. Mac is still typical: happy, carefree, good-natured, but with a mind that works entirely on Indian time. I rode behind him as we walked our wiry Indian ponies up the long Topocoba Trail. Occasionally he sang. He never looked around to see if I was there. It never occurred to him.

The Land of the Sky Blue Water faded and dissolved into the background. At Hilltop you step across the door into your own world. I was sorry to leave Supai. It had been a pleasant interlude. I couldn't live there permanently; I shouldn't want to—yet it is a delightful place. Anyone who loves the Grand Canyon country, or any part of the American West should try to see it. Do it soon. The chief business of Supai is to go on being Supai, but anything may happen.

Dismounting, I waited for the mail truck to arrive from Grand Canyon village thirty-five miles away. Mac waited, too, for he would pack the mail down on his return trip. We had nothing much to say to each other and Mac never speaks unless he has something to say. I gave him a sandwich.

"Thanks," he said, and put it in his pocket.

"Going to take it home to your kids?" I asked.

"Yep," he said.

"How many kids have you, Mac?"

"I got eight."

"That's a pretty good record," I said.

"Yep," smiled Mac.

"How old are they?"

"All same age," said Mac.

"Can't be," I said. "I'm talking about your kids, not your pups."

"Eight kids," averred Mac. "Four boys and four girls."

"How old are they?" I asked.

"All different," said Mac.

"Can't be," I said.

"Got girl eight years old," said Mac.

"How old is your boy?"

"All kids age eight, savven, seeks, five, four, three, two, wan," explained Mac slowly.

"Well," I said. "You'll have to try for little Zero. Where's he?"

"He's comin'," said Mac with assurance.

The mail truck came at the same time.

VI

North Rim

Kaibab Country

FOR many centuries the Paiute Indians called it the Kaibabits, which means "mountain lying down"; more recently white men called it the Buckskin Mountains; and President Theodore Roosevelt proclaimed it the Kaibab National Forest in 1908. The name has three syllables—pronounced Ky-a-bab. When the Grand Canyon National Park was created in 1919 a large part of the Kaibab country was included, stretching along the North Rim from Marble Canyon on the east to Kanab Creek on the west. It is a vast imperious noble region of untouched beauty, ranging from an elevation of eight thousand feet at Bright Angel Point on the rim, to points well above ten thousand on the upper reaches of the Kaibab plateau. It supports flora both delicate and rugged and fauna ranging from the lion to the mouse.

It is not very well known to the American public for several reasons but particularly for its remoteness and elevation. Those who visit the Kaibab must do so between May and October as heavy snows blanket the area the remaining six months. And those who visit it must make a special effort to do so as it is definitely off any main transcontinental highway and no railroad is closer than two hundred miles. Furthermore those who visit it seldom go beyond the reaches of the automobile and much of the Kaibab country is inaccessible by motor car. If you have a yearning to see America as it was before there were white Americans, here it is.

The North Rim of the Grand Canyon is quite unlike the South Rim. It is one thousand feet higher and therefore in a different life zone. As the earth slopes from north to south at this point, and as the Grand Canyon has cut across this sloping plain from east to west, most of the tributaries come into the Colorado River from the north. This means that the North Rim has many large side canyons (Bright Angel, for example) which would be major scenic attractions in themselves if they weren't surpassed by the main gorge itself.

To get to the North Rim, I suggest driving from the South Rim by way of the Painted Desert in the Western Navajo Reservation, Lee's Ferry Bridge (called Navajo Bridge) over the Colorado River, House Rock Valley, and Jacob Lake. This is a thrilling drive of unsurpassed beauty; and if you are geologically minded you will be doubly fascinated. If you choose to approach the North Rim from Utah, the Union Pacific will take you as far as Lund, Utah, by train, and on from there by bus. If you prefer to come in your own car, the roads are excellent, but remember that this area is closed in the winter months. Once at the North Rim you will find the same variety of accommodations for all kinds of pocketbooks as are available on the South Rim—you may have a well-appointed modern bungalow or a cabin, or you may pitch a tent or roll up in a sleeping bag.

A terse description of the North Rim is impossible. In contemporary "bobby-sox" English it is something "super-duper." From various points you can look across at the South Rim about ten miles away and because of your elevation you look completely over it. The South Rim is somewhat diminished in importance from your point of view, and at sunset it is often back-lighted. If you are lucky enough to see a thunderstorm in action, in the canyon and over on the other rim, it will be quite a show. From your Olympian advantage you will see the rain pouring down in various parts of the canyon below while you stand in sunshine. Zigzags of lightning flash and snap from rim to river and thunder rolls over the serried peaks and reverberates through the canyons below. It is cataclysmic and for the nonce you are not a man, but a god.

With all of these highly dramatic elements, however, the North Rim is somewhat more peaceful than the South. The forests are deep and rich and because of the extra thousand feet in elevation, there are Douglas firs, aspens, blue spruce, red birch and mountain mahogany; while it is mostly piñon pine on the South Rim, with no trees comparable to the stately and magnificent Douglas firs, protected and nurtured in their youth by the "quaking" aspens. These lovely aspens, by the way, were first described as "quaking" by French Canadians who have a legend that the cross of the martyrdom of Jesus was made of aspen wood and that is why the tree has always trembled. Its destiny is to repent forever. There have been religious zealots who refused to work in a camp where aspen wood was used for fuel. Actually, it is not a durable wood. The tree lives only about fifty years and its lightness precludes its being used except for paper pulp and light wooden cartons. Since we are on the subject of aspens, it may be pointed out that the wood, having no taste or odor, makes good containers for lard or butter, should you be seeking a lard or butter container.

The Kaibab country has little or no historical lore. The Paiutes were here for centuries. Up until 1870, it was known only by a few trappers and hunters, and following them came the cattlemen. These latter were representatives of the Mormon Church. The Church, in a pioneer pump-priming project, to increase the resources of its people, put livestock on the Kaibab plateau. Once established, the Church sold the enterprise to individuals. This business was more or less effectually spiked by Washington in 1893 when President Benjamin Harrison signed a bill creating the Grand Canyon Forest Reserve. With the establishment of the National Park in 1919 livestock gave way to a national development of recreation and scenic values. The Kaibab country now belongs to the people of the United States.

There is no rim drive on the north side comparable to that of the south. But there are several drives that are certainly worth taking, and they follow the contour of the long side-canyons and embayments. The three points which, for stunning grandeur should not be missed, are Cape Royal, Point Imperial, and Point Sublime. They are all beyond verbal description. At Angel's Window, near Cape Royal, the drop is so precipitous and the ledge so narrow that it is unsafe to stand out there in a strong wind. If this kind of thing bothers you, stay in your car on the extremely safe roads. But do not fail to take the short hike from the main lodge to Bright Angel Point overlooking a canyon known as The Transept which is a side-canyon of Bright Angel, which, in turn, is a side-canyon of the Grand Canyon.

From Bright Angel Point you will note four peaks forming a chain of mountains to the east of Bright Angel Canyon which is at your feet. They have a remarkable sequence of names which are: Zoroaster Temple, Brahma Temple, Deva Temple, and Uncle Jimmy. I'm not sure that Major Powell's penchant for Oriental names was the happiest factor in naming these peaks and mesas, but as long as there is the down-to-earth Uncle Jimmy there seems to be a balance.

Uncle Jimmy himself (James Owens) was a completely balanced character indeed. He was a Kaibab pioneer, mountaineer, lion hunter, and professional guide. I believe I am correct in stating that Uncle Jimmy was Theodore Roosevelt's guide during some lion-hunting expeditions back in 1913. T. R. loved the Kaibab country and thoroughly enjoyed himself in it. It is not on record that he ever got any lions, but Uncle Jimmy got plenty.

Not being hunting-minded I cannot vouch for the claims of the Kaibab as being a peerless hunter's paradise. But it does have a wide variety of animal life, none of which I have ever shot.

The oddly named mule deer are plentiful. There are some on the South Rim, but the Kaibab is their habitat. They are often tame (a big help to amateur hunters, no doubt) except in the mating season when the bucks get assertive, possessive, and even dangerous.

There are a few bighorn mountain sheep, but they stay in the remotest canyons and on the sides of the most rugged peaks and are a most rugged sheep. Rarely are they seen.

Buffalo were brought to the Kaibab Plateau in 1905; they didn't like it and bolted to the warmer area of House Rock Valley. As you approach or leave the Kaibab by this route you may see them grazing peacefully and totally disinterested in man.

Of lagomorpha (rabbits to us) there are some in the lower and warmer regions. Paiutes will eat them when they can catch them, but that is rare too.

Rodents are in heaven: squirrels, chipmunks, woodrats, kangaroo rats, many types of mice—from the desert mouse of the lower zones to the meadow mouse of the Canadian zone—gophers, porcupines, and beavers. The Albert squirrel lives on the South Rim, and the husky Kaibab squirrel with his all-white tail lives on the North Rim. This all-white tail is said to be an example of the Lamarckian theory of naturally acquired characteristics. In the heavy snows during the winter, this squirrel can curve his white tail over his gray body and thus blend or camouflage himself with the background. His relatives on the South Rim have less of a snow problem, and nature and evolution have not given them white tails.

And where there are rabbits and rodents there will be carnivorous animals to prey upon them. The outstanding is the Kaibab lion. A large male will weigh as much as two hundred and seventy-five pounds, and that's a hunk of cat. Rodents are but hors d'oeuvres to him. He attacks the deer and lives on them. Once the lions were hunted so persistently that they decreased in number and the deer were able to increase too rapidly and began to run out of forage. Nature casts a balance of forces, and of supply and demand, and man does well not to tamper too much with either.

Besides the meat-eating lion there is the bobcat common to both rims. The gray timber wolf once lived on the Kaibab, but has just about been decimated.

Coyotes are present, as they are everywhere in the West. There is a gray fox on both rims and down in the canyon. Also there is a ringtail cat. This prowler seldom comes up to the rims, but one aggressive individual adopted El Tovar Hotel as his home and used to prowl the dining room where the Fred Harvey girls fed him. Naturally he said to hell with the canyon and stayed on the South Rim where he became quite a fixture and pet. It was a startling sight to see this slinking beast walk along an upper molding casting his yellow eyes on the various tables and twisting his ringed tail.

There are raccoons and opossums and weasels and skunks and badgers and moles and otters. And there are bears. These are extremely rare, but at one time the black bear lived on the Kaibab Plateau. Many years ago a huge grizzly bear was killed on the North Rim by an Indian boy who saw him first. It is the only one on record. We could go on into the orders of insects and bats and birds, but I think that here at least zoology should go just so far and no further.

To match the eleven trails that drop from the South Rim to the river there are but four on the North Rim and only one of these is advisable unless you are a professional in trail blazing. This is our old friend the Kaibab; dropping from the South Rim to the suspension bridge and continuing to Phantom Ranch, it winds up the long Bright Angel Canyon and finally "tops out" on the North Rim. Thus it is not too difficult to go from rim to rim, but only Superman could do it in one day. If you make this rim-to-rim trip, however, you can really say, "I've seen the Grand Canyon" with reasonable assurance. But it would be like completing one semester of a Freshman course and saying, "Oh, yes, I've been to college." There still will be a lot more to see.

Since the Kaibab Trail crosses the suspension bridge, a little history of this unique structure is in order.

To the enterprising try-anything-once Mormons goes the credit of bridging the Colorado in its canyon region. The idea was conceived about 1900 by a man named D. Wooley and was in progress by 1903. Dave Rust, Mr. Wooley's son-in-law, was in charge of operations, and his chief trouble was in getting the cable down the trail on the backs of mules. It was not until 1907 that the first cable was placed across the river. A small cage suspended from above was trammed across by other cables fastened to the main cable. This cage was just large enough to hold one horse or mule. Rust set up a camp, as a base of operations, near the mouth of Bright Angel Creek. This was given the obvious and unimaginative name of "Rust's Camp," and some peach, apricot, and plum trees were planted and thrived. It was the beginning of what is Phantom Ranch today.

The suspended cage was always precarious, and one day a horse went berserk during transit, kicked open the cage door, jammed the cable, half fell out, and finally hung out. Nothing could be done so a hardy soul named Robert Vaughn had the courage to climb out on the cable hand over hand over the murderous Colorado River and cut the rope, freeing the horse. The animal plunged to its death in the violent river below.

The release of this weight caused the main cable to spring up and down and Vaughn was all but flung loose. Somehow he managed to hang on and, with supreme effort, got back again, hand over hand, to safety.

When Theodore Roosevelt visited the Kaibab country in 1913 and was not chasing lions with Uncle Jimmy Owens, he camped at Rust's. T. R. was then an ex-president and he is the only ex-president, or president for that matter, who has been put in a cage and sent dangling over the Colorado River.

Later the cage was supplanted by a rickety suspension bridge. This flimsy contraption would sag and sway with the weight of a mule. Ranger Edward R. Laws who has lived in the Kaibab country over fifty years tells a story about this swinging catwalk that gave him chills. It seems that the rule was established that only one mule at a time should cross. More than one on the bridge might plunge the whole business into the river. Laws arrived with seven mules and attempted to get his leader mule to walk across. The other six waited. The leader mule didn't like the idea and he didn't trust the bridge. Mulelike, he refused to risk his neck; he wouldn't budge. Laws cajoled and kicked but the mule was unmoved. When Laws sat down exhausted the mule looked around at him and promptly decided to cross the bridge of his own volition. Laws was horrified to see all six of the others immediately follow the leader. He held his breath as all seven mules nonchalantly plodded across the creaking swaying structure—nothing happened. Once across, they all looked back and waited for him to follow. Mules are truly wonderful. They have a perverse and devilish sense of humor.

In 1928 the Park Service scrapped the old flimsy catwalk and built the present suspension bridge supported by eight one-and-one-half-inch cables anchored to the rock walls of the inner gorge. But when you cross on this perfectly safe structure seventy feet above the river give a thought to Rust's overhead tram and its big improvement, the swaying catwalk. You'll appreciate the present bridge a lot more.

There is another North Rim trail which is a continuation of a South Rim trail, but unlike the Kaibab, it has different names on each side of the river. This is the Bass Trail on the South Rim, seldom seen by tourists, and is the Shinumo Trail on the North Rim, probably never seen by tourists. It was built by W. W. Bass as described in the chapter "Trail-Wise and Trail-Weary." In 1900 Bass developed a small orchard and garden near the mouth of Shinumo Creek. He called it Shinumo Gardens and he crossed the river by means of a boat controlled by a cable. The trail is in poor condition today and is not recommended by the Park Service. What is left of it ascends Shinumo Creek and vaguely melts into the Kaibab country at the North Rim near Powell Saddle. These are points rarely seen by the average tourist.

A third North Rim trail is the Nankoweap. This, again, is a remote region, difficult to reach and more difficult to leave. To the east of the Kaibab highlands lies a huge saucer known as the Nankoweap Basin. Down into this primitive country goes the Nankoweap Trail and it is practically impassable today. It was built in either 1880 or 1882 (authorities disagree) by Major Powell's men in an effort to provide a route from rim to river for a geological survey party. It was tough and thankless work, and after seventy-two days of trail-building the party left the area to survey elsewhere. The trail remained and was presumably used, if not maintained, by the horsethieves who comprised the "Grand Canyon Horse and Mare Company." When this band of outlaws was broken up, the Nankoweap Trail ceased to serve anyone. Portions of it have disappeared and unless it is rebuilt in the future, the little-known Nankoweap will pass into Grand Canyon history.

One North Rim trail remains, and that is the Thunder River. This is quite a distance west from the lodge and not easy to reach. It is a good forty miles from Bright Angel Point to Big Saddle Camp. Somewhere nearby, although nobody agrees with anybody else, the Thunder River Trail begins. Ranger Laws describes it as descending Tapeats Canyon but says that "the country is so wild over that way that places and names don't mean much." He says that Paiute Indians used it originally as far down as the Supai formation, and in 1926 he constructed the lower part down through the redwall to the river. It is in poor condition today.

Ranger Laws probably knows from first-hand experience as much as, if not more than, any other individual about the North Rim of the Grand Canyon. You'll have to search for him as he is not an aggressive man, but a friendly visit will be more than worth your time. He was born Edward Robert Laws in the tiny Mormon town of Johnson, Utah, a little more than half a century ago. His father's name was Wildcat, according to the Paiutes, because he was a hunter and trapper and skinner of mountain lions. At the age of nine Ranger Laws carried the mail from Kanab, Utah, to Lee's Ferry, Arizona, a horseback ride of eighty-five miles, and accepted in that wild country as a likely job for any nine-year-old boy. He can tell you many a story of the early days in the Kaibab country, and all of them are true.

There is another "local boy who made good" in this area. His positive personality and ready smile will win you and he won't let you have a dull moment. You are not likely to find him at the Union Pacific lodge at Bright Angel Point, but are almost sure to find him at Kaibab lodge about eighteen miles north of the rim. This is a particularly beautiful part of the Kaibab country. Major Powell called it de Motte Park in 1872 (after a professorial member of his party) and later it became the famous V. T. Ranch—the initials standing for two cattlemen, Valentine and Townsend according to Ranger Laws, and for Van Slack and Thompson according to the guidebook. The impact of the personality you'll find here will be softened a bit by some of the signs on the way. These read: "Campers—go to Hades" and "Want horses? Go to Hades" and "Deer hunters go to Hades" and "Your stay will be one of the most enjoyable if you'll go to Hades"—and the like. Believe it or not, you are about to meet a man whose name is Hades Church.

For your hikes and walks and stories about the North Rim see Ranger Laws; but for your horses and side trips into the wilder Kaibab, go to Hades. Mr. Church (a term of address you'll never use) is the owner of Big Saddle Camp, and this retreat is "on the edge of hell and gone," according to Hades, in the heart of the Kaibab, two miles from the canyon rim. In season at Big Saddle you can rent a cabin and rest or spend your time chasing lions (letting the lions chase you is more fun for the lions, according to Hades) or hunting deer or fishing or playing at being a cowboy by roping calves and branding and riding broncs and eating at the chuck wagon. "Bring old clothes," says Hades. "We're as informal as hell. We welcome old shirts but this is no place for stuffed shirts." He's right. "Ladies are welcome," he advises. "I've got nothing against them. Fact is, I had a wife once, but I couldn't keep up the payments of one horse a month, so the Navajos came and took her back. Let's go!" That's the Kaibab country if you're interested.

Thunder River and Toroweap

I DOUBT if a dozen white men have ever been to Thunder River. And I know only of one who has made his way from its source to the confluence with the Colorado, one man in a nation of something like one hundred and forty million. He is Jonreed Lauritzen of Arizona.

From the start let it be clear that I have never seen Thunder River. World War II put a stop to my research and made any further expeditions into the remote areas of the North Rim impossible. Accommodations, supplies, horses, and mules were no longer obtainable, and even if they had been, I was put into a uniform. Then why include Thunder River in this chapter? Simply because it cannot be overlooked in a comprehensive book on the Grand Canyon area, and because I have been able to gather enough information about this phenomenon to make it worth telling by reflected light.

I have talked to men who have been to Thunder River. If they could write books on the Grand Canyon, I'd leave it to them. But they can't, and it seems essential to include some information about this section by attempting to cull the truth from various impressions. Therefore we'll look through the eyes of Ranger E. R. Laws and Mr. Hades Church, a pair of seeing-eye dogs for our blindness. No better guides could be found. In fact, I have read accounts in print about Thunder River by an American novelist of great fame whose books have sold into the millions. He described Thunder River in detail, but throughout his lifetime he didn't get as close to it as we'll get in this chapter.

The very existence of Thunder River was unknown until 1904, and the trail to the river was not made until 1926. Nobody knows who named it, but all agree on the name. It is a roaring, plunging, dashing torrent that comes crashing and smashing its violent way down a side-canyon of the Grand Canyon. Apparently its entire course for many miles is one of furious cascades and falls. And this is no mere creek like the delightful Bright Angel; this is a real river gone mad in its surge toward its master, the Colorado. Ranger Laws describes it as at least three times the width of Bright Angel Creek which means it is conceivably seventy-five feet across, if not more. Hades Church thinks it is wider than that. Its speed is estimated at thirty miles an hour—and for a river that's equivalent to jet-propulsion. It is mostly locked tight in the vise of the canyon it has created and throughout the major part of its rampaging course it is boulder-strewn. Where there are wider cleavages in the canyon walls, there are maidenhair ferns, lichens, primroses, mimulas, cottonwoods, and birch; and, coming down to the river but keeping a safe spray-distance away are the inevitable desert flora of cat's claw, greasewood, burro bush, and cactus. The river is too restless in its turgid whirling and plunging to have much effect beyond its high-water mark on the adjacent earth. And its roar is such that conversation beside it is impossible.

Ranger Laws declares that Thunder River is the greatest sight in the canyon country apart from the main gorge itself. Hades Church, usually extravagant in his descriptions of anything, gets very humble and says, "They haven't made up the words yet that can describe it." Jonreed Lauritzen uses "fierce majesty" and continues with "the human mind cannot even grasp what it sees here."

There is considerable difference of opinion about the source of this river, but none about its destination. Everyone agrees that Thunder River rushes madly into the tawny coffee-colored Colorado where its frantic silver water is lost in the greater stream.

As to its source, that's a disputed subject. Ranger Laws describes it as gushing forth from a canyon wall and crashing one hundred and fifty feet in the first plunge of its mad course. Hades Church says it pours out of a solid ledge of rock, falls five hundred feet, and then races on more or less as described. Jonreed Lauritzen, in a carefully written article in *Arizona Highways* magazine, states that it "springs mildly from among the rocks" near the head of its canyon. Everyone may be right, for no man has seen Thunder River at all seasons of the year. It is possible that it varies exactly as it has been described.

Whoever named it did a good job; had it been called Jones Creek or O'Brien River it would have lost a great deal of its romantic appeal. Major Powell, who was quite a hand with nomenclature, and who saw only the confluence of Thunder River with the Colorado, called it Tapeats Creek in 1871 (after a Paiute Indian he employed) and Frederick S. Dellenbaugh, in his *Canyon Voyage* published in 1908, described the mouth of it as "a fine, clear, cold creek larger than the Paria River." On at least one map it is identified as Tapeats Creek but Thunder River it is certain to be called over any other name.

A trip from the mouth of Thunder River to the top of the Kaibab Plateau can be done now only by foot. In the future the trail may be improved, so that horses or mules can make it. If so, it will be worth your while (and mine to see how nearly my information is correct) to make this vertical cross-section of the North Rim. In so doing you will pass through nearly every one of the arbitrarily defined life zones of the northern hemisphere.

A word about these zones is timely in relation to Grand Canyon topography. In 1889, Dr. C. Hart Merriam of the United States Biological Survey noted the determining factor of altitude in relationship to life. In other words, types of life, both plant and animal, showed a relationship between latitude as measured in miles on the flat surface and altitude as measured in feet. A latitudinal division offering a definite type of life was considered by Dr. Merriam as a life zone and for every latitudinal division there was a corresponding altitudinal division. Thus the Grand Canyon and Dr. Merriam developed the life-zone theory which has since been accepted by most biologists throughout the world.

The theory is based on the supposition that a difference in elevation of one thousand feet may be considered the equivalent in its effect on plant and animal life to the normal change of three hundred to five hundred miles of latitude at sea level. There are seven major life zones from equator to pole; and there are seven corresponding zones in altitude. Very generally they are as follows:

Tropical—sea level to 2000 feet
Lower Sonoran—2000 feet (the mean altitude of the Colorado River in the canyon bottom) to 4000 feet
Upper Sonoran—4000 feet to 7000 feet
Transition—7000 feet to 8000 feet
Canadian—8000 feet to 9000 feet
Hudsonian—9000 feet to 11,000 feet
Arctic—Above 11,000 feet

Five of these seven life zones are therefore found from the river to the highest point on the Kaibab Plateau. The Tropical is not in the Grand Canyon's repertoire, but the other extreme, the Arctic, may be found only a short distance away where the San Francisco Peaks of north-central Arizona protrude up into the Arctic zone. Thus the overall Grand Canyon area embraces, in general, six of the seven possible life zones. There are many contributing factors and modifying conditions, but in the main, the theory is completely practical. Anyone who has studied it, even slightly, can take a look from his Pullman window or from his own car, on any railroad or highway in the United States, and within reasonable margin, make a guess as to his height above sea level in relationship to his distance north of the equator.

Remote as the Kaibab country and Thunder River may be, there are still other parts of the Grand Canyon's North Rim which are even more difficult to reach.

One of these is Toroweap Point.

The Toroweap valley and canyon are not in the Grand Canyon National Park but in the Grand Canyon National Monument which is contiguous and merely an arbitrary projection of government control along the North Rim which no doubt eventually will be included in the park itself.

To get to Toroweap today is not at all impractical if you'll accept two tire tracks across mesa country instead of a highway. And the route to Toroweap is sufficiently attractive in itself to make any lover of the West happy. Toroweap Point is about sixty airline miles due west of Bright Angel Point, but it is a drive of little more than one hundred and fifty miles by car. There is only one way to go but you can very easily lose your way and drive on into the Antelope Valley and arrive nowhere but the Antelope Valley. Before you get this far, however, you will drop down the north slope of the Kaibab country beyond Jacob Lake which is nearly 8000 feet above sea level to the sunbaked Arizona hamlet of Fredonia which is about 4800 feet above sea level. This town is almost on the Utah state line and you are in a section known as Arizona's "strip," an area geographically and culturally removed from the South Rim and the rest of the state, and included therein only because of the hard-and-fast, arbitrary, straight-line boundaries of most Western schemes of survey as determined after what Bernard de Voto astutely calls the year of decision, 1846. This "strip," which is larger than the State of Massachusetts, is sparsely settled country pioneered by Mormons, and for all practical purposes the area should have been included in Utah. In fact, the North Rim of the Grand Canyon might well have been the southern boundary of Utah save for the fact that it was not so designated on a drawing board in Washington.

At Fredonia you leave the highway on a fair enough road through the Kaibab Indian Reservation (Paiute Indians, of course) to Pipe Spring. This is a National Monument in its own right, and not to be confused with Pipe Creek on the lower Bright Angel Trail on the South Rim. Pipes, obviously, figure in the history of both, and the name was the result of a jest in both cases. Pipe Spring has had its share of violence and tragedy. Washington made it a national monument in 1923 as a memorial to the fortitude of the Western pioneer.

History and christening began at Pipe Spring in 1856. A party of Mormons camped there. The leader was Jacob Hamblin who seemed to be as well traveled around Utah and Arizona in those days as George Washington on the Eastern seaboard in the Colonial period. For once, however, it was not Jacob who held the center of the stage, but another member of the Hamblin family. This fact has been lost in history and the naming of Pipe Spring is usually credited today to Jacob. He was merely a spectator.

It was "Gunlock Bill" (William Hamblin and brother of Jacob) who was taken in by a trick bet. He was told he was

such a poor marksman that he couldn't puncture a silk handkerchief at fifty paces. Now Gunlock Bill was a crack shot,
very proud of it, and inclined to be touchy about any deroga-
tory remarks. He accepted the bet.

Upon firing at the handkerchief from fifty paces and hit-
ting it in the bull's eye if there had been a bull's eye, Gunlock Bill was chagrined to find that the silk, fastened only by
its upper edge, yielded to the force of the bullet. He could not
puncture it after all, and lost his bet.

Childish shenanigans of this kind were regarded as the
cleverest type of humor on the frontier. But quips and cranks
and wanton wiles did not amuse Gunlock Bill when they were
pulled off at his expense. He pouted. The others laughed all
the louder. Bill became angry; and as his reactions were those
of a twelve-year-old, he followed through with twelve-year-old
cunning. He bet one of the party that he could shoot the bowl
from this man's pipe at fifty paces and never touch the rim.
This wager was accepted. Bill took aim and shot the pipe to
pieces. It was his turn to laugh. As to the rim, he never
touched it, and nobody else would ever touch it again either.
Bill felt better and they decided to call the place Pipe
Spring.

Later, in 1866, two ranchers, Whitmore and McIntyre, the
former with an eight-year-old son, lived at Pipe Spring. Either
Navajos, or Paiutes, or both, stole cattle from under their
noses. The two men left the boy in a dugout at Pipe Spring,
rode in pursuit of the Indians and straight into an ambush
and were killed. The Indians returned to Pipe Spring wearing
the clothes of the murdered men, and somehow overlooked
the boy hiding in the dugout. The following day the boy
started on foot for St. George, Utah, nearly a hundred miles
away, but luckily met some Mormons only ten miles from
Pipe Spring. Several days later Mormon militia, out for
justice, came upon Indians wearing the clothing of Whitmore

and McIntyre. Justice was quick; the Indians were shot. Then it developed that these were innocent Indians who had merely traded with others for these desirable clothes, not knowing they were getting "hot goods." The real criminals escaped and the tragedy of errors came to an end.

In order to put a stop to further Indian depredations, Bishop Anson P. Winsor arrived from Salt Lake City in 1870, and built a fort over and including the spring. It was a stout building of red sandstone, two stories high, with an interior courtyard and a firing parapet. It was intended to withstand a siege, and moreover, the spring was within the fortress. Now let the red devils come and get picked off from above. The red devils, very sensibly, never attacked.

For many years this edifice was known as Winsor Castle. It is the museum and monument that commemorates today a little-known chapter in a little-known part of the West.

The road from Pipe Spring to Toroweap is a road by name only. If you are used to the rough roads and wagon tracks of the Indian country, you'll get through but if you insist on a paved and signed highway with a painted streak down its middle, you'd better not go for a few years or more. Once you are headed in the right direction (south) and keep the Hurricane Cliffs of the Uinkaret Plateau on your right, you'll arrive in time at Tuweep Post Office, elevation 7700 feet, and you will have completed your great loop from the Kaibab through northern Arizona and will be back in the Grand Canyon country again. It is about fifteen miles farther to Toroweap Point.

Here is one of the most stunning spots in the world. You'll be more than a mile (about six thousand feet) above the Colorado River; the walls of the inner gorge of the Grand Canyon are closer here than at any point farther east; and the entire experience is one that you cannot believe is possible. After all you have seen of Grand Canyon vistas, the devil and the angel have one more knockout punch to throw at you and this is it. It is an individual experience and only individual reactions are possible. Neither my words nor yours will matter. Here is something to take your breath away, literally and figuratively. There is no describing Toroweap Point. With that I'm sure any visitor will agree. Take a good look.

About the Toroweap valley, however, it is possible to say something. The attractive name, translated from Paiute, means nothing more than Greasewood valley or Greasewood canyon. The post office called Tuweep is a meaningless contraction, a compromise, simply because Washington didn't choose to name a post office for a point according to one version, or intended to name a post office for a point and became confused about pronunciation and spelling according to another version. The valley is in the Transition life zone, or between seven and eight thousand feet above sea level. At one time it supported a comparatively abundant Indian population, but this was back in the days of what ethnologists call Pueblo II, or the second subdivision of the great Pueblo culture, about 900 A.D. to 1100 A.D. There are ethnologists who believe there is sufficient evidence to show that the Toroweap region also supported the Basketmaker culture perhaps as far back as 300 A.D. Since these pre-Columbian civilizations, life at Toroweap has been pretty skimpy. A few ranches have been homesteaded and abandoned. It is a tough country to conquer and the winters are often severe. Some sheep have been grazed in it, but there is not enough water to make it profitable or practical. The floor of the valley abounds in greasewood, dwarfed yucca, cactus, sagebrush, and other typically high desert flora. It had, during my exposure to it, a wonderfully invigorating air, and entirely apart from the nearby Grand Canyon, the valley has a beauty of its own—a kind of raw, stark, uncompromising power. The Grand Canyon National Monument, of which Toroweap is a part, is administratively the most recent section to come under federal control—the area being taken over in 1932.

To stand at Toroweap Point is a requisite for anyone who wants to qualify for the degree of Grand Canyon graduate. It is the last and highest class that the school has to offer. And for a final examination, as your commencement in fact, when you are about to leave this institution forever, there is a way out which will not be by the same door where you came in.

West of Toroweap is Mount Trumbull. It is 8700 feet above sea level, and as the valley slopes up toward this peak the life zone begins to change from Transition to Canadian. This is the farthest western portal of the Grand Canyon country. If you save this for the last exit, you can leave knowing that you've seen a great deal—not all—but a very great deal indeed. The road will doubtless be poor, and poor is too mild an adjective. But somehow you cannot resent anything as superficial as a bad road, or no road at all.

Once there was a tiny settlement west of Mount Trumbull called Bunneyville. Don't count on it for anything for it has become a ghost town. You are in wild untouched country and there is nothing but hard driving between you and the Mormon town of St. George, Utah, one hundred miles to the northwest. You have turned your back on the great gorge. Ahead lie such typically Western names as Poverty Hill, Solitaire Butte, and Wolf Hole. You've said good-bye to your friend the Grand Canyon.

The Dirty Devil and The Bright Angel

THIS book ended with the preceding chapter, and save for a few trifling facts about the Grand Canyon, it is not necessary to read any further.

On the other hand, it is impossible to leave a phenomenon like the Grand Canyon merely by turning away from it. In a Wordsworthian sense it has "thoughts that do often lie too deep for tears." The intrinsic significance, the triple-distilled essence of the Grand Canyon to an inquiring mind is simple; but it is a simplicity made up of complexities.

I've called the canyon a dualism and at times a schizophrenic. This is especially true in view of the antics of the river—although river and canyon are inseparable. Men who study the canyon are forever touched by it. Certainly this was true of Major Powell from the first time he saw it; and he expressed it in nomenclature, especially in the Dirty Devil and the Bright Angel.

Powell was a scholar first and last. The Grand Canyon for him was a university. It had its lasting effect upon him, culminating in a planned trilogy of three volumes in which he proposed to explore and examine the organized knowledge of man. Only one of the books was published. It was called *Truth And Error* or *The Science of Intellection*, and appeared in 1898, published by the Open Court Publishing Company in Chicago. Its seed fell on stone partly because it was poorly distributed, partly because it was difficult to read, and partly because it was ahead of its time. In its final paragraphs this sentence occurs, "The philosophy here presented is neither idealism nor materialism; I would fain call it the philosophy of science."

Powell's second volume reached manuscript stage before his death in 1902, but if it was ever published it has long since gone to rest in the purgatory of the out of print. In it he included chapters on the relations of primitive people to environment, folklore, aboriginal mythology of the American Southwest, anthropology, human evolution, esthetology, philology, and immortality. The reading public was not interested.

The third volume remained a dream.

What Powell was seeking was truth, and he went after it in the best scientific manner. The Grand Canyon was his laboratory. This search for truth is one aspect of religion. It is, in fact, more than one aspect for it is the meaning and goal of the religious instinct. In this sense the Grand Canyon was not only Powell's laboratory, but his cathedral.

In his first contact with the canyon country Powell ran into the dualism of devil and angel. This was the result of too short a perspective. He stepped back and saw farther. Devil and angel became one. In his later writings, his point of view is beyond good and evil, black and white, idealism and materialism, devil and angel. He had an overall idea by the tail but he was never able to subdue the animal itself.

At the base of the Coconino sandstone on the North Rim there is the ruin of a large cliff dwelling. Once it was two stories high and fragments of its pottery are strewn along the talus slope below the sandstone. At one side there is a ceremonial kiva. Louis Schellbach, ranger-naturalist, estimated this ruin as the last phase of Pueblo II, or from A.D. 900 to

1100. This area is known as the Powell Saddle. The inquiring philosopher-scientist-major will be known by such landmarks long after his scholarship is forgotten.

When the first staggering impacts of the Grand Canyon have been tempered with understanding it will no longer be devil or angel. The personal point of view offers no yardstick by which to measure it. You can't criticize it or change it. The balance of nature is there. The history of the earth is there; plant, animal, and mineral evolution are there, and nothing can be done about it. All you can do is take it in and try to understand it.

The Park Service strives admirably to keep the scheme of things as natural forces demand. To some extent control is possible, but any attempt at change runs into trouble. Lightning, for example, may cause a forest fire in the Kaibab. The Park Service can put the fire out. Aspens will grow in the burned-out area. These will offer shade and protection to the smaller seedling pines and spruce and firs. But when the Park Service protected the deer in the Kaibab, they increased and their forage diminished. So the deer ate the aspen seedlings, and thus checked the pines and the spruce and the fir. In turn, the deer had to be checked. Predatory animals were allowed to feed on the deer. Hunting was permitted and some fawns were even shipped out of the area—all to preserve the balance of nature.

Somebody decided that all dead and unsightly trees should be removed, forgetting that insects live in dead trees. For jays eat the insects and at the same time jays will carry pine seeds up hill and bury them. Thus a pine forest can in time spread uphill which it could not do if there were no dead trees and hence no insects and hence no jays. By removing the unsightly dead trees the forest would spread only downhill until it reached the lower limit of its life zone and then it would eventually disappear. So you just can't do anything about the Grand Canyon except let it alone.

You have to see both the devil and the angel and reach an overall point of view. Then the Grand Canyon will give you a lot of clues as to the meaning of meaning. It can be just a hole in the earth or it can be a religious experience. Edwin Creighton in *An Introductory Logic,* wrote, "We assume that the world is a cosmos and not a chaos [and you can substitute Grand Canyon for world]. And this means that there are universal relations and connections of events which, if once discovered in their true nature, may always be depended upon."

The logician is correct as far as he goes, but who can say with finality what is "true"? A biologist, J. B. S. Haldane, wrote, "When we realize that in our observing the 'blue' sky we are also making it blue, our attitude to the 'nature' which we see around us becomes very different." This hearkens back to good Berkeleyism—"To be is to be perceived." You can keep on along this track until you discover that there is no Grand Canyon at all and its existence is only predicated upon your perception of it. And that may be "true." If so, it is we ourselves who create the sky and the canyon and the devil and the angel and good and evil and all other dualistic forms.

I believe Powell got this far. He came out of the cathedral a little wiser than when he went in. Some men can do the same with science or religion or philosophy or all three. Some perpetually see only the devil and the angel and believe in them; others come to understand that the devil and the angel are only limited perceptions and that their meaning or truth or what have you, lies beyond.

So let the Grand Canyon speak to you; listen with an open mind, long and attentively. Apart from what it yields of history, geology, ethnology, archaeology, paleontology, anthropology, and any and all other "ologies" representing divisions of the classified knowledge of man, the Grand Canyon has something to say—to you.

Index

INDEX

INDEX